A Field Guide to Oklahoma's Amphibians and Reptiles

By Greg Sievert and Lynnette Sievert

Photos by Greg Sievert

Edited by
Lesley B. Carson, Design Editor
and Mark D. Howery, Technical Editor

Front cover photos: (clockwise from upper left-hand corner) Texas Horned Lizard, Spring Peeper, Northern Rough Greensnake, Stinkpot, Barred Tiger Slamander

The Wildlife Diversity Program - a program of the Oklahoma Department of Wildlife Conservation - monitors, manages and promotes rare, declining, and endangered wildlife, as well as common wildlife not fished or hunted. Oklahomans help fund the Wildlife Diversity Program through an annual state income tax check-off, the purchase of wildlife conservation specialty license plates, product purchases, and individual donations.

The printing of the first edition in 2005 was funded in part through the federal Wildlife Conservation and Restoration Program under grant number R-9-E. The printing of the second and third editions was made possible by the Oklahoma Department of Wildlife Conservation and Wildlife Diversity Program supporters.

The authors would like to dedicate this book to Dr. Jeffrey H. Black, who was a friend and co-author of A Field Guide To Amphibians of Oklahoma. Jeff studied Oklahoma's amphibians for many years, and he was especially fond of Oklahoma's frogs and toads. We miss our discussions of Oklahoma amphibians and forays into the field with Jeff.

ABOUT THE AUTHORS

Greg Sievert has spent many years observing and photographing amphibians and reptiles. He received both his B.S. and M.S. at Eastern Kentucky University in biology. Greg is an accomplished photographer and has photographs on numerous books, magazines, journals, and newsletters. His photographs also appear on several posters. In 1999 Greg won the prestigious Suzanne L. and Joseph T. Collins Award for Excellence in Kansas Herpetology for his photograph of an Eastern Gray Treefrog. Greg was an active member of The Oklahoma Herpetological Society during the seven years the Sieverts lived in Oklahoma, and he served as president of the organization for two years. He is now a member of the Kansas Herpetological Society and has served as its president for one year. Greg has over 30 years of teaching experience including herpetology, biology for non-majors, and ecology. He has been an instructor at Emporia State University for the last 14 years.

Lynnette received her B.S. in biology from Buena Vista University in Iowa, her M.S. in biology from Eastern Kentucky University and her Ph.D. in zoology at the University of Oklahoma. She spent a year as a post-doc in a biochemistry lab at Auburn University. For five years she was an Assistant Professor of Biology at Maryville College in Tennessee. Lynnette is now Professor of Biology at Emporia State University in Kansas where she has served as a major professor and a member of numerous graduate student committees. Lynnette studies environmental physiology of amphibians and reptiles. She is a member as well as board member of the Kansas Academy of Science, a member as well as editorial board member of the Kansas Herpetological Society, a member of the American Society of Ichthyologists and Herpetologists (ASIH), a member and board member of the Society for the Study of Amphibians and Reptiles (SSAR), a member and past treasurer of The Herpetologist's League and former member of the Oklahoma Herpetological Society.

The Sieverts have taught herpetology in Oklahoma (OU), Tennessee (Maryville College), and Kansas (Emporia State University). They have published numerous scientific papers and have served as reviewers for many scientific journals.

AUTHOR CONTACT INFORMATION

Greg Sievert and Lynnette Sievert
Emporia State University
Department of Biological Services
1200 Commercial Street
Emporia, KS 66801-5087
gsievert@emporia.edu
lsievert@emporia.edu

Contents

FIGURES

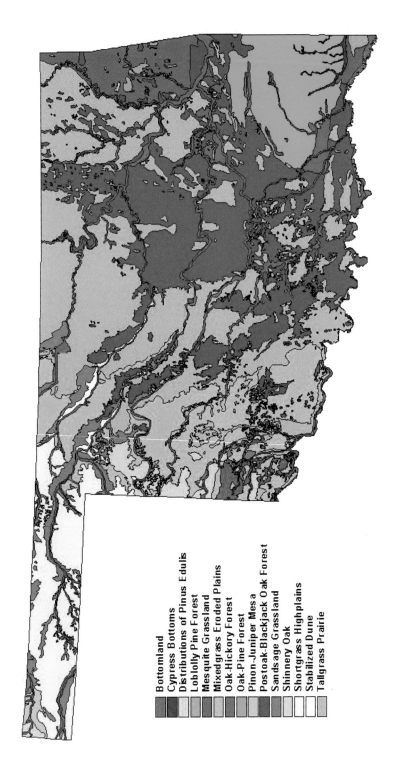

Oklahoma Habitat-type Map (Duck and Fletcher, 1943) Oklahoma Department of Wildlife Conservation

Bottomland
Cypress Bottoms
Distributions of Pinus Edulis
Loblolly Pine Forest
Mesquite Grassland
Mixedgrass Eroded Plains
Oak-Hickory Forest
Oak-Pine Forest
Pinon-Juniper Mesa
Postoak-Blackjack Oak Forest
Sandsage Grassland
Shinnery Oak
Shortgrass Highplains
Stabilized Dune
Tallgrass Prairie

INTRODUCTION

We have chosen to write this book as an introduction to the interesting world of amphibians and reptiles for the general reader. This book contains information to help you identify Oklahoma's 58 amphibian and 99 reptile species and subspecies. A glossary of terms at the back of the book defines scientific terms that may be unfamiliar to you. We have included the meanings of some of the scientific names where we thought it would be helpful or of interest. Species accounts are arranged by taxonomic group, and within taxonomic groups, they are arranged alphabetically by genus then species, except when a two-page account could not be kept on facing pages. For more detail on genus and species, see taxonomy section below. Since species are not arranged by appearance, you may need to look through every account within an animal group to find species that look alike. The sizes given at the top of each account are sizes of mature adults. In this edition are descriptions of some of the frog and toad breeding calls and a few of Oklahoma's distinct tadpoles that are fairly easy to identify.

Oklahoma has a unique mixture of amphibians and reptiles because of its diverse habitats ranging from coastal plains to high mesas and central location in the United States. Only three other states plus Oklahoma have more than 10 ecoregions (see page vi.). Oklahoma's climate produces wide variations in seasonal and daily temperature and moisture conditions. Many amphibians and reptiles reach their eastern, western, northern, or southern range limits here. The distributional patterns of Oklahoma's amphibians and reptiles are complex with many species meeting barriers that prevent range expansion. Interstates 35 and 40 are close approximations of these boundaries in some cases.

RANGE MAPS

Herpetologists (scientists who study amphibians and reptiles) have no way of finding and tracking every amphibian and reptile in Oklahoma. The range maps we have constructed for each species in this book are based upon the combined efforts of Greg Sievert, Mark Howery and Julianne Hoagland and are based upon museum records and documented sight records. The range maps drawn for each species include only the counties in which the senior author (who is solely responsible for any errors) believes they currently exist, rather than where they could be found based on similar habitat, as in *A Field Guide to Amphibians of Oklahoma* and *A Field Guide to Reptiles of Oklahoma* editions. In this edition we did not include the Round-tailed Horned Lizard or the Intermountain Wandering Gartersnake because the senior author believes their range no longer includes Oklahoma. In addition, we have added the recently described Cajun Chorus Frog. Certain outlying counties were omitted from some of the range maps either because they were based on a sight record or the museum record was more than 25 years old and the senior author does not believe they exist there any longer. Therefore, the ranges of many of the amphibians and reptiles in Oklahoma appear smaller than they did in *A Field Guide to Amphibians of Oklahoma* and *A Field Guide to Reptiles of Oklahoma*. The ranges of all species are dynamic and new information is collected each year regarding the distributions of reptiles and amphibians. As new records are collected, these should be shared with the Oklahoma Biological Survey, which maintains the Distribution of Oklahoma Amphibians and Reptiles by Recorded Sightings (DOKARRS) databases, and the scientific community. It is likely that the placement of voucher specimens into curated museum collections will further clarify the actual ranges of Oklahoma's amphibians and reptiles.

AMPHIBIAN AND REPTILE BASICS

Like humans, amphibians and reptiles are vertebrates and share nearly all of the same body parts and functions. They have a spinal cord and backbone, a well developed nervous system, brain, and senses of touch, vision, hearing, taste, and smell. Some lizards have better vision than we do. Contrary to myth, snake and lizard tongues cannot sting people when flicked. Rather, the tongue brings in small molecules that can then be sensed by a special sensory organ that humans do not have. Oklahoma's rattlesnakes, Copperheads, and Cottonmouths are able to detect prey using heat-sensing pits. These pits are located between and below the eye and nostril on either side of the head. Aquatic amphibians have a series of sensory structures called the lateral line for sensing movement in the water. Amphibians and reptiles have a lower metabolism (calorie use) and therefore require less food than mammals. Unlike mammals, amphibians and reptiles use behavioral means such as basking and shade seeking to control their body temperatures. During periods of activity, many reptiles have body temperatures similar to ours and so it is incorrect to refer to them as "cold-blooded." The proper term is ectothermic, which means that these animals get most of their heat from an external source such as a warm rock or by basking.

CONSERVING OKLAHOMA WILDLIFE

The reptiles of Oklahoma are inoffensive and try to avoid human contact. Only nine of the 60 species and subspecies of snakes are venomous to humans and none of the other amphibians or reptiles are venomous to humans. Sadly, habitat loss and unnecessary killing of snakes and turtles have reduced their numbers. Perhaps if time were taken to watch and study these unusual creatures humans would more readily accept them. Landowners can conserve these rapidly disappearing creatures as well as other wildlife species by providing water and shelter, creating fishless aquatic habitats, and increasing cover. Many of the amphibian species breed in ponds without fish. Introducing fish to these ponds can cause a rapid decline in amphibian numbers since the fish eat both the eggs and larvae of amphibians or compete with them for food or space.

Some amphibian and reptile species have different habitat needs at different times of the year. Fragmentation of the environment makes it difficult for these animals to move safely from one habitat to another without excessive risk. Corridors of undeveloped land between habitats can reduce risks to animals as they move from winter to summer habitats.

Introduction of non-native animals and plants can have an adverse effect on native amphibians and reptiles. Promoting diversity of native plant species and leaving native vegetation along the edges of rivers, streams, and ponds is helpful to native animals. Protecting and restoring wetlands also promotes the welfare of Oklahoma's amphibians and reptiles.

Many amphibians and reptiles spend their inactive time under cover objects such as fallen logs, snags, woody debris and so forth. Removal of these objects can have a negative impact on wildlife populations. Excessive use of pesticides and fertilizers also can be harmful to amphibians and reptiles, because of the toxic nature of these chemicals and run-off into water supplies used by these animals. Intense grazing also alters grasslands and has a negative impact on amphibians and reptiles. The best thing for a landowner to do if an area already supports a healthy population of amphibians and reptiles is to leave the land as it is.

The Oklahoma Department of Wildlife Conservation's Wildlife Diversity Program, The Nature Conservancy, The Oklahoma Natural Heritage Inventory, and other organizations are attempting to identify, purchase, and protect valuable wildlife habitats throughout the state to ensure that future generations will be able to see Oklahoma's native amphibians and reptiles as well as other wildlife species.

LAWS PERTAINING TO OKLAHOMA'S AMPHIBIANS AND REPTILES

Some of the amphibians and reptiles in Oklahoma have closed hunting seasons or are classified as Species of Special Concern. These designations mean that these species are less common within our state's borders and should not be removed from their natural habitat. These species are noted in the individual species accounts. To legally catch other amphibians and reptiles one must have a valid Oklahoma hunting license to collect terrestrial amphibians and reptiles or a valid Oklahoma fishing license to collect aquatic amphibians and reptiles. Check the current Hunting Guide, produced by the Oklahoma Department of Wildlife Conservation, for specific regulations and details.

AMPHIBIAN AND REPTILE NAMES

Animals are divided into groups based on genetic similarity and their evolutionary history. Genetically similar, potentially interbreeding individuals make up a species. Some species have multiple populations that, while being very similar to each other, have distinguishable differences. These populations are called subspecies. One example is the milksnake for which three subspecies occur within the state of Oklahoma.

GENUS	SPECIES	SUBSPECIES	COMMON NAME
Lampropeltis	*triangulum*	*syspila*	Red Milksnake
Lampropeltis	*triangulum*	*gentilis*	Central Plains Milksnake
Lampropeltis	*triangulum*	*amaura*	Louisiana Milksnake

Usually the geographic ranges of subspecies overlap and individuals from both subspecies may interbreed. In areas where two subspecies overlap, there may be individual animals that show physical characteristics of both subspecies. These areas are sometimes referred to as intergrade zones. Although not all biologists feel it is important to recognize subspecies, they are included in this book for completeness.

To identify an amphibian or reptile, compare it with the book's illustrations and photographs, read the accompanying description, and examine the range map. If this information accurately describes the amphibian or reptile you are trying to identify, you have probably correctly identified the species. If the description and photograph match the species but the specimen was found outside of the range map's boundaries, you may have misidentified the animal or discovered a range extension in Oklahoma for that species.

SCIENTIFIC AND COMMON NAME CHANGES

Some of the scientific names of Oklahoma's amphibians and reptiles are currently being debated as more information on the evolutionary history and genetics of these animals becomes available. Much of these data and proposed taxonomy changes are based on mitochondrial DNA analysis. We feel it is just one character in a suite of characters that should be used in determining the taxonomic status of a species or subspecies. As all scientists know, all of these new taxonomic arrangements are only hypotheses proposed by the publications' authors. For the most part, we are using the scientific and common names published by the Society for the Study of Amphibians and Reptiles Committee on Standard English and Scientific Names, Brian I. Crother, Chair (2008). It is Herpetological Circular #37 and entitled, "Scientific and Standard English Names of Amphibians and Reptiles of North America North of Mexico, with Comments Regarding Confidence in our Understanding." This list of scientific and standard names has been adopted by the American Society of Ichthyologists and Herpetologists, The Herpetologists' League, and the Society for the Study of Amphibians and Reptiles. The problem with this list and the competing list by Collins and Taggart (2009) is that the subcommittee members readily accept new taxonomic changes based on mitochondrial DNA and/or DNA analysis. One example is *Elaphe*, which was changed to *Pantherophis* (the Bullsnake) then lumped into *Pituophis* with the Bullsnakes, then split out into *Scotophis*. This seems to promote taxonomic instability and chaos, and in the end separates species from their previous literature. In addition, recent publications using the new taxonomy may be based on uncritical acceptance of these new changes because they appear in one of the two competing standard names lists. We feel that a state field guide is not an appropriate venue for arguing the pros and cons of name changes. Therefore, we have included the proposed name changes in the remarks section of each species in question, but have retained the older recognized taxonomy. We also do not agree with the use of the word "common" in common names because it may refer to a species abundance. Therefore we did not use Common Checkered Whiptail because it is not common in Oklahoma. Also, changing common names like Woodhouse's Toad to Rocky Mountain Toad, New Mexico Spadefoot to Chihuahuan Desert Spadefoot, Great Plains Narrow-mouthed Toad to Western Narrow-mouthed Toad, and Stinkpot to Eastern Musk Turtle seemed confusing and unnecessary.

ACKNOWLEDGMENTS

The authors would like to thank the many individuals who helped to make this book possible. John MacGregor and Dr. R. Wayne VanDevender were instrumental in improving and encouraging the senior author's amphibian and reptile photography. They provided many useful discussions on photography, herp photography techniques, and have accompanied the authors on many photographic field trips. Dr. R. Wayne VanDevender, Victor "Butters" Tuttle and Joey P. Holmes helped acquire amphibians and reptiles to photograph for this book. Joe Branham provided valuable assistance in choosing photographs to be used in this edition. Bill Smith provided housing, field assistance, and camaraderie when the authors were photographing in the Ouachita Mountains.

Richard Lardie graciously shared his range map data for the amphibians and reptiles found in Oklahoma. Curtis Schmidt plotted museum and DOKARRS (Distribution of Oklahoma Amphibians and Reptiles by Recorded Sighting) records onto maps for each species. Mark Howery and Julianne Hoagland drew the final version of the species range maps.

The following people provided range map extensions for many species in this edition: Robert Bastarache, Dr. Joe Bidwell, Brandon Bourassa, Bruce Burton, Richard Butler, Dr. Janalee Caldwell, Scott Cox, Larry Daniels, Bill Fesperman, Gene Gilliland, Aaron Goodwin, Joe Grzybowski, Mark Howery, Tandy Keenan, Shane Lowe, Ray Moody, Clayton Porter, Corey Roelke, Curtis Schmidt, Don Shepard, Dr. Tim Patton, Dr. Laurie Vitt and Chad Whitney.

The authors owe a huge debt of gratitude to Dr. Stanley Fox. This book was greatly improved by the editorial assistance of Dr. Fox and his former students: Joe Hackler, Jerry Husak, Kris Karsten, Day Ligon, Aaron Place, Matt Rouse, Paul Shipman and Pam Widder.

The authors also thank Karla Beatty, Joe Branham, Mike Branick, Dr. Janalee Caldwell, Doyle Crosswhite, Neil Garrison, Dr. Don Glass, Julian Hilliard, Micah Holmes, Richard Lardie, Dr. Mike Mather, Jenny Thom-Hester, Rebecca Rezula and William Ray for their reviews and helpful suggestions. Thanks also to Dr. Carl Anthony, Dr. Robert Clarke, Dr. Richard Highton, Dr. George Pisani, Daren Riedle and Dr. Laurie Vitt for assistance with some of the accounts.

Thanks also go to the Oklahoma Herpetological Society for contributing funds for the production of the first edition of this book and to the following donors:

Tulsa Audubon Society
Tulsa County Conservation District
Tulsa Zoo Conservation Program
The Noble Foundation
The Nature Conservancy, Oklahoma Chapter
The Wildlife Society, Oklahoma Chapter
Payne County Audubon Society
Richard L. Lardie

Central Oklahoma Grotto Society
Cans 4 Critters Participants
Joe Branham
Oklahoma Clean Lakes Association
Outdoor America Store/F.B.F. Inc.
Oklahoma Conservation Commission
Oklahoma City Zoo & Botanical Garden

We would also like to acknowledge the individuals who provided editorial comments on earlier editions of *A Field Guide To Amphibians of Oklahoma* and/or *A Field Guide to Reptiles of Oklahoma*: Dr. Mike Mather, Dr. Charles Carpenter, Randy Baker, Joseph T. Collins, Richard Lardie, Dr. William Carter, and Dr. Jeff Black.

Mark Howery, Lesley B. Carson, Ben Davis, Kristen Gillman, Kelly Murrah and Micah Holmes of the Oklahoma Department of Wildlife Conservation also provided a great deal of assistance with many aspects of this book.

Checklist of Amphibians and Reptiles
(157 species and subspecies)

Amphibians of Oklahoma
(58 species and subspecies)

SALAMANDERS (24 species and subspecies)

FROGS AND TOADS (34 species and subspecies)

REPTILES OF OKLAHOMA

(99 species and subspecies)

ALLIGATOR (1 species)

TURTLES (19 species and subspecies)

LIZARDS (19 species and subspecies)

9

AMPHIBIANS

Salamanders

SALAMANDER OR LIZARD?

Salamander body shapes are similar to those of lizards, especially skinks, but the two kinds of animals differ in many ways. Lizards have scales, dry skin, claws, and most have ear openings. Salamanders have smooth, moist skin, lack claws, and lack ear openings. Lizards frequently bask whereas salamanders do not. Salamanders are active primarily at night whereas our native lizards are active during the day.

BEHAVIOR

None of Oklahoma's native salamanders are venomous or pose a threat to humans or pets. Only the large, aquatic species could bite hard enough to break the skin. Most amphibians have mucus-producing glands in their skin, and it is wise to thoroughly wash your hands after handling these animals, especially before you touch your eyes or mouth. All salamanders are carnivorous and mainly eat small invertebrates including insects, worms, and spiders.

Salamanders are secretive amphibians that are rarely encountered above ground and in the open. They spend most of their time in moist habitats under rotting logs and leaf-litter, underground, in caves, or in streams and ponds. If they are removed from their moist habitat they can rapidly dehydrate and die. Most Oklahoma salamanders are active at night, especially during and after rains. Many species have color patterns that allow them to blend in with their natural habitat.

ANATOMY

All salamanders use one or more of the following three types of respiration: skin respiration, lung respiration, and gill respiration. All species have relatively thin, moist skin and are capable of taking up oxygen directly through the skin. Oxygen is absorbed into the many small blood vessels beneath the skin's surface and distributed throughout the body. For many terrestrial salamander species, the larvae respire through external gills (see Fig. 1b and 1c) while the adults have lungs. Some aquatic species, including the sirens, can use gills, lungs, and skin breathing simultaneously.

Most salamanders have four toes on the front feet and five toes on the hind feet. Costal grooves (see Fig. 1d), along the sides of most salamanders, indicate the position of their ribs. The number of costal grooves between the front and hind limbs can be used to help identify these salamanders. Both larvae and adults have similar diets and consume small invertebrates. Usually the larvae and adults do not have similar coloration and the larvae lack eyelids, which are present in most adults. The *Caudata* are Oklahoma's tailed amphibians.

REPRODUCTION

Unlike frogs, which call to attract females, salamanders lack calls but have elaborate courtship rituals. Males and females perform dance-like courtships. Following courtship, the male releases a sperm packet (spermatophore) that is picked up by the female and stored in her spermatheca until the eggs are ready to be fertilized. Females deposit the eggs in a moist area or in water. Some species leave the eggs and provide no care for the young, while other species watch over their eggs. Depending upon the species of salamander, the eggs either hatch into aquatic larvae that later metamorphose or hatch into miniature replicas of the adults (see Fig. 1).

CONSERVATION

Although salamanders and their larvae are preyed upon by many wildlife species, humans pose the greatest threat. Pesticides that kill insects and other small invertebrates deplete their food source and may poison the salamander. In addition, habitat destruction and the draining or removal of wetlands and temporary pools can eliminate local populations.

GROUPS OF SALAMANDERS

Oklahoma has six groups of salamanders. Sirens retain gills and remain aquatic throughout their lives. Sirens have small eyes and front legs and completely lack hind legs.

Amphiumas, like the sirens, are fully aquatic over their whole lives and lack eyelids. Amphiumas are large salamanders with powerful jaws that can inflict a painful bite, however, they are rarely encountered and pose no threat to humans.

Mudpuppies retain gills and remain aquatic throughout their entire lives. They can reach a large size. Eggs hatch into tiny mudpuppies that look like the adults.

Newts have a unique life cycle that includes a terrestrial eft stage between the aquatic larval and aquatic adult stages. Larvae and adults look similar except that the adults lack gills.

The mole salamanders are widely distributed in Oklahoma. Larvae lack the adult coloration and do not resemble the adults. These salamanders are most frequently observed during rains when they cross roads to get to breeding ponds. Most species breed in the spring, but a few breed during the fall.

Adult lungless salamanders lack both gills and lungs, so respiration occurs through the moist skin. These salamanders are restricted to moist woodlands in eastern Oklahoma. A distinguishing trait of this group is the nasolabial groove (see Fig. 2), which sits between the lip and nostril. The lip is tapped on the ground or other object of interest. This allows odor particles to move up the nasolabial groove and into the nose for chemical processing. Some Oklahoma lungless salamanders are black with white spots and are difficult to identify unless you know what part of the state they inhabit. Male *Plethodon* salamanders have a round mental gland under the chin that is used in courtship. The mental gland produces chemicals that stimulate the female to court and mate. Salamanders in the genus *Plethodon* lay eggs that hatch into juveniles that resemble miniature adults and do not pass through an aquatic larval stage. This is called direct development. Species of the genera *Eurycea*, *Desmognathus* and *Hemidactylium* have aquatic larvae.

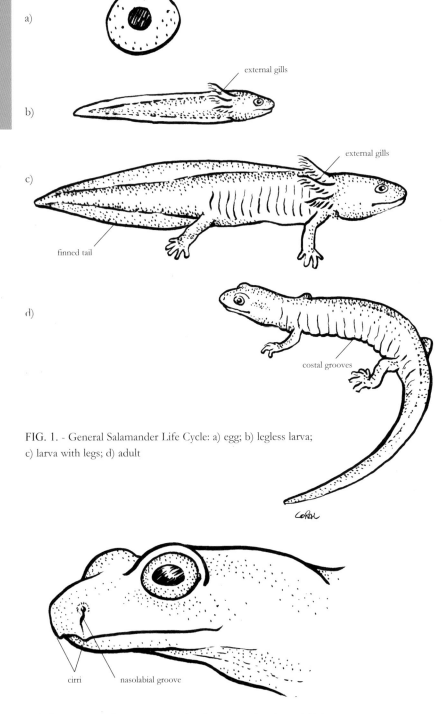

FIG. 1. - General Salamander Life Cycle: a) egg; b) legless larva;
c) larva with legs; d) adult

FIG. 2. - Head of lungless salamander showing cirri and nasolabial groove

Western Lesser Siren
Siren intermedia nettingi

Head showing external gills

SIZE: 10-19 inches

APPEARANCE: It is a long, slender, aquatic salamander that has front legs with four toes, but no hind legs. The Siren has a flattened head and squarish snout. The external gills (see Fig. 1c) are red to gray. Its back color varies from light brown to black and may have dark spots or flecks. The belly is a pale cream color. A young Siren has one or two yellow stripes down each side of the body and a broad light colored stripe on each side of the head.

SIMILAR SPECIES: The Three-toed Amphiuma and the Red River Mudpuppy both have front and hind legs. The Three-toed Amphiuma does not have external gills. Eels (fish) have fins and no legs.

FOOD: Insects, crayfish, worms, and snails.

HABITAT: Swamps, oxbows, lakes, marshes, roadside ditches, and sluggish water with aquatic vegetation and plant debris in the coastal plain region of southeastern Oklahoma.

REMARKS: If the habitat dries up, a Siren burrows into soft mud and secretes a mucus, parchment-like cocoon that dries around all of its body except the head. The cocoon greatly limits dehydration and allows the Siren to estivate until water returns. A Siren has both lungs and gills, but the lungs are used mostly for buoyancy. The Siren is a unique amphibian in that it has a four chambered heart. A Siren can emit clicking or yelping sounds when disturbed or handled. During the day these salamanders remain inactive and hidden in dense vegetation or muck. Males aggressively defend mates and many males and females have bite marks on their bodies during the breeding season. This salamander is nocturnal. This animal is named for a mythological creature, the siren. In Oklahoma, this is a Species of Special Concern and cannot be taken from the wild.

Three-toed Amphiuma
Amphiuma tridactylum

Head close-up; note three toes on left foot

SIZE: 18-30 inches

APPEARANCE: It is Oklahoma's longest salamander. It has a somewhat pointed snout, small lidless eyes, and four tiny limbs each with three toes. Adults lack external gills. Its back and sides vary from dark brown to black while the light gray belly color extends up the sides of the body and meets the dark back.

SIMILAR SPECIES: The Lesser Siren lacks back legs and the Red River Mudpuppy has much larger, thicker legs and has external gills. Eels (fish) have fins and no legs.

FOOD: Crayfish, mussels, tadpoles, small fish, salamanders, and frogs. It will eat almost anything that is moving and small enough to fit in its mouth.

HABITAT: Swamps, oxbows, roadside ditches, backwaters, marshes, sloughs, and other standing water with aquatic vegetation and debris in the coastal plain region of southern McCurtain County.

REMARKS: This species is the main food item for the rare Western Mudsnake that lives in the same habitat. This large salamander is harmless but can inflict a painful bite. There is no truth to the myth that this species is venomous. If the habitat dries up it will estivate in crayfish burrows or tunnel deep into drying mud. Eggs are laid on land near water and when the rains come in the fall the eggs are flooded and then develop and hatch. The female stays with the eggs until hatching. An Amphiuma is nocturnal. The name *tridactylum* means three-toed. In Oklahoma, this is a Species of Special Concern and cannot be taken from the wild.

Red River Mudpuppy
Necturus maculosus louisianensis

SIZE: 8-13 inches.

APPEARANCE: It is a large aquatic salamander with long red to gray external gills (see Fig. 1c) four well-developed legs, and feet with four toes. It has a long fin-like tail and a gray, yellow, or rust dorsal color usually with scattered dark spots or blotches. A dark line extends from the nostril through the eye to the gills. The belly is cream to white with large, dark, spots and blotches. The center portion (midline) of the belly is often unmarked.

SIMILAR SPECIES: A Lesser Siren lacks hind legs. The Three-toed Amphiuma has four tiny legs and no external gills. Eels (fish) have fins and no legs.

FOOD: Crayfish, worms, insects, snails, leeches, amphibians, and small fish.

HABITAT: Rivers, large streams, lakes, and below the dams of reservoirs. During the day it hides in mats of leaf litter in backwater areas or under flat rocks in swift water.

REMARKS: This salamander retains gills throughout life and breeds as an aquatic larval-like form. The Mudpuppy breeds in the late fall or winter, but eggs are laid several months later in the spring. Eggs are attached in a group under a rock in the streambed. The female Mudpuppy tends the eggs, which increases their likelihood of hatching. Fishermen occasionally catch this inoffensive salamander below dams or in rivers and lakes; they should remove their hooks and return Mudpuppies to the water. A Mudpuppy has well-developed legs and although it can swim, often moves by walking along the bottom of the water. This species is nocturnal. Siltation and pollution have caused a decline in some populations. Myth has it that this salamander barks like a dog, though it makes no sound, hence the common names waterdog and mudpuppy. Some believe this salamander is venomous, but it is not. The term *maculosus* means spotted.

Central Newt
Notophthalmus viridescens louisianensis

Adult

Terrestrial eft

18

SIZE: 2-4 inches.

APPEARANCE: The mostly aquatic adult is dull yellowish-brown or olive green with a contrasting yellow belly. The back and belly are covered with small black dots. A dark line runs from the nostril to the eye and back to the front limb. This line is not seen in the eft stage. An adult has a flattened, fin-like tail, no costal grooves (see Fig. 1d) or external gills, and somewhat rough skin. The eft (land dwelling life stage) is reddish-orange to yellowish-brown, has less black spotting, rough skin, and a roundish tail. The larva looks like an adult except it has gills.

SIMILAR SPECIES: Other terrestrial salamanders have smooth skin and costal grooves.

FOOD: Prefers earthworms but also eats snails, insects, small crayfish, and amphibian eggs.

HABITAT: In or around ponds, pools, swamps, or roadside ditches in moist woodlands.

REMARKS: This salamander's life history varies from other species. Eggs are laid singly on underwater vegetation. Eggs hatch into aquatic gilled larvae that transform into land-dwelling efts. After one to three years, the efts change into semi-aquatic adults, although some individuals can remain as efts for a longer period. The adults usually remain active all year long and can sometimes be seen swimming under the ice of a frozen pond or swamp. During the spring breeding season, the males have swollen vents, black toe tips, and black pads and ridges on the inner surface of the thighs. Newts, especially efts, have skin glands that produce foul-tasting chemicals that discourage predators from eating them. The bright skin color of the eft warns potential predators that the eft is unpalatable. Efts can be found under rotting logs or piles of leaves. This species can be active any time of the day or night. The name *viridescens* is in reference to the green color. A recent taxonomic study indicates that the currently recognized subspecies of newts from the eastern United States do not agree with groupings derived from molecular data. Further research is needed to elucidate the taxonomic status of the newt found in Oklahoma.

Aquatic adult

Ringed Salamander
Ambystoma annulatum

Aquatic larva

SIZE: 5-7 inches.

APPEARANCE: It is the most slender, elongate ambystomatid salamander in the state. It usually has 15 costal grooves (see Fig. 1d) and a dark brown to black dorsal color with well-separated yellowish to white rings. The rings may be broken to form bars and may not completely reach the belly. The belly is yellow to gray with small white specks. There is a light gray, irregular stripe along the lower part of the body and sometimes a grayish transverse bar between the eyes.

SIMILAR SPECIES: The Marbled Salamander is chunky and black with broad white bars that go only part way down the sides, has a plain black belly, and only 11 costal grooves. The Barred Tiger Salamander is larger, robust rather than slender, has 11-14 costal grooves, and a black and yellow body.

FOOD: Earthworms and other invertebrates.

HABITAT: Moist woodland areas.

REMARKS: This nocturnal salamander is rarely seen except during heavy rains in the fall when it moves to ponds, swamps, and roadside ditches to breed. Occasionally it can be found under logs during the breeding season. Courtship occurs in ponds when large numbers of males and females have arrived. The males swim around, frequently bumping into each other, and then deposit spermatophores. The female is enticed to pick up the spermatophores during courtship. Courtship and egg laying last only a few days and then the adults leave the pond. Eggs are deposited singly, in small strings, or in small masses mostly on the pond bottom but can be attached to aquatic vegetation. This salamander has a spotty distribution. The name *annulatum* means ringed. It does not do well in captivity and should not be kept as a pet. In Oklahoma, this is a Species of Special Concern and cannot be taken from the wild.

Spotted Salamander
Ambystoma maculatum

Aquatic larva

SIZE: 6-8 inches.

APPEARANCE: This chunky salamander has a black back with two rows of bright, round yellow to orange spots. These spots extend from behind the eye to the end of the tail. The belly is dull gray with white specks. There are normally 12 costal grooves (see Fig. 1d).

SIMILAR SPECIES: The Barred Tiger Salamander has a yellow and black belly and yellow bars or blotches rather than spots. The Eastern Tiger Salamander has pale blotches that are not all round. The Marbled Salamander has a black belly and white or gray bars across the back.

FOOD: Earthworms, insects, snails, and spiders.

HABITAT: Moist forested areas and in ponds or pools in more open areas.

REMARKS: During heavy spring rains, Spotted Salamanders can be seen crossing roads, sometimes in large numbers, on their way to breeding ponds or pools. An adult returns to the pond it was hatched from each year to breed. After the spring breeding season this nocturnal salamander is rarely encountered. This species sometimes has a symbiotic relationship with algae that grow on the eggs and make them look green. Since the algae provide oxygen for the embryos, there is decreased mortality and an increased hatching rate. A threatened adult will often lash its tail at the predator. The name *maculatum* means spotted.

Barred Tiger Salamander
Ambystoma mavortium

Adult

Gilled larval form

Gilled larval form

SIZE: 6-9 inches.

APPEARANCE: This salamander has dark brown to black dorsal color with bright cream or yellow bars extending from the belly onto the back. The belly is mottled with black and yellow. It has a broad, round snout and 12 or 13 costal grooves, but occasionally 11 or 14 (see Fig. 1d) are present. In arid areas, where the ground outside the pond is not suitable for burrowing, the Barred Tiger Salamander can become an aquatic adult with external gills (see Fig. 1c). The aquatic adult is plain olive to brown and can reach a length of 14 inches. Both aquatic and terrestrial adults reproduce.

SIMILAR SPECIES: The Eastern Tiger Salamander has pale dorsal blotches.

FOOD: Worms, grubs, insects, fish, amphibians, and anything live that is moving and small enough to fit in its mouth.

HABITAT: Adapted to a wide variety of habitats: cattle troughs, ponds, and caves in the arid areas of western Oklahoma.

REMARKS: This nocturnal species is the most widespread salamander in Oklahoma. It is the largest terrestrial salamander throughout its Oklahoma range. It may be found in gypsum caves. The Tiger Salamander does quite well in captivity and is a voracious feeder. The larval form of this salamander is sometimes incorrectly referred to as a waterdog or mudpuppy, which is the common name of the true Mudpuppy, *Necturus maculosus*. The gilled larvae are common in western Oklahoma ponds and are sometimes caught on hook and line by fishermen.

* A recent scientific study split the Barred Tiger Salamander and Eastern Tiger Salamander into separate species.

Color and pattern variation

Marbled Salamander
Ambystoma opacum

Aquatic larva

SIZE: 3-4 inches.

APPEARANCE: This is a plump salamander with a plain black belly and light, mostly saddle-shaped crossbars on the black back and tail. The male's crossbars are normally white, whereas the females are typically gray. There are usually 11 or 12 costal grooves (see Fig. 1d).

SIMILAR SPECIES: The Barred Tiger Salamander is larger and has a black and yellow belly. The Ringed Salamander has 15 costal grooves, a light belly, mostly complete rings over the back, and a slender build.

FOOD: Earthworms and other invertebrates.

HABITAT: Moist woodland areas.

REMARKS: In the fall after mating, the female lays her eggs under a log or other cover object near a pond or temporary water source. She guards the eggs and waits for heavy fall rains to raise the water level and flood the eggs. The eggs won't hatch until flooded. If there is not sufficient autumn rain to flood the eggs, they may overwinter and hatch after spring rains. Guarding the eggs increases the likelihood that they will survive. If threatened, it may coil its body and lash its tail at the threat. This species is nocturnal.

Mole Salamander
Ambystoma talpoideum

Aquatic larva

SIZE: 3-4 inches.

APPEARANCE: This is a short, plump *Ambystoma* that has a gray, brown, or black dorsal color with whitish flecks or indistinct mottling. The gray belly is marked with light spots. The slightly keeled tail may have a light gray stripe along the top. The Mole Salamander has a large head that is relatively large and wider than the neck, giving it the appearance of having plump cheeks. It has fairly long toes on the hind feet, a short tail, and 10 or 11 costal grooves (see Fig. 1d).

SIMILAR SPECIES: The Small-mouthed Salamander has a longer body and 14 or more costal grooves. Also, the Small-mouth Salamander's head is smaller and approximately the same width as the neck.

FOOD: Insects, snails, and earthworms.

HABITAT: Moist lowland forests.

REMARKS: This nocturnal species is restricted to extreme southeastern Oklahoma and is rarely encountered except during the spring on its way to or from breeding ponds. It lives underground most of the year and sometimes resides in crayfish or mammal burrows. Very little is known about the Oklahoma population of Mole Salamanders. The name *talpoideum* means mole-like and refers to the burrowing lifestyle of this species. It is an Oklahoma Species of Special Concern, and is protected by state law and cannot be removed from the wild.

Small-mouthed Salamander
Ambystoma texanum

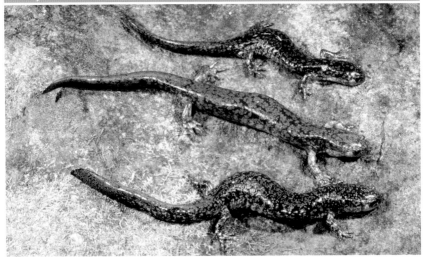

Color variation

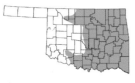

Aquatic larva

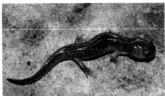

Juvenile

SIZE: 4-6 inches.

APPEARANCE: The back is dark brown to black with markings ranging from small, light colored flecks to larger, indistinct silver or white mottling. The dark belly may have small gray flecks. Some individuals are plain brown to black with no flecking while others may be extremely lightly pigmented on the sides of the body. It has a slender head, small mouth, and elongate body. An adult has 14 to 15 costal grooves (see Fig. 1d). The male is smaller than the female, but the male has a longer tail.

SIMILAR SPECIES: A Mole Salamander has a head that is wider than the neck, giving it the look of having jowls. The Mole Salamander only has 10 or 11 costal grooves.

FOOD: Earthworms, slugs, spiders, and insects.

HABITAT: It can tolerate many habitat types ranging from moist forest to moist prairie.

REMARKS: This is the second most widespread salamander in Oklahoma. It breeds after rains in the spring in shallow, fishless waters. The eggs are laid singly or in small groups attached to underwater vegetation or sticks. It can be found almost every month of the year after heavy rains, but is easiest to find in the spring and fall. When disturbed it may raise its tail and wave it from side to side. Albino specimens have been reported from the Oklahoma City area. This species is nocturnal.

Aquatic larva

SIZE: 6-9 inches.

APPEARANCE: The Eastern Tiger Salamander is a large, dark salamander with faded orange, yellow, or light greenish dorsal blotches or spots. The belly is dark and mottled with yellow blotches. It has a broad, round snout and 12 or 13 costal grooves, but occasionally 11 or 14 (see Fig. 1d) are present.

SIMILAR SPECIES: The Spotted Salamander has smaller, paired yellow spots and a speckled belly. The Ringed Salamander is smaller, more slender, has mostly complete rings over the back, and has 15 costal grooves. The Marbled Salamander has white or off-white markings and a plain black belly.

FOOD: Worms, grubs, insects, fish, amphibians, and anything that is moving and small enough to fit in its mouth.

HABITAT: Moist woodlands and caves in eastern Oklahoma.

REMARKS: This nocturnal species is one of the largest terrestrial salamanders in Oklahoma. The Eastern Tiger Salamander does quite well in captivity and is a voracious feeder. The larval form of this salamander is sometimes incorrectly referred to as a water-dog or mudpuppy, which is the common name of the true Mudpuppy, *Necturus maculosus*. It frequently inhabits limestone caves. The name *tigrinum* refers to the yellow and black color pattern.

*A recent scientific study split the Eastern Tiger Salamander and Barred Tiger Salamander into separate species.

Ouachita Dusky Salamander
Desmognathus brimleyorum

Young adult showing color variation

SIZE: 3-5 inches.

APPEARANCE: This is a robust salamander with a light to dark brown dorsal color, a plain yellowish to light brown belly, and 14 costal grooves (see Fig. 1d). It may have a faint line from the eye to the angle of the jaw and a sharply keeled tail. Juveniles have a pattern of light spots or blotches on the back and may have rows of faint spots along each side. In older adults the dorsum becomes plain dark brown. The neck is wider than the head and the back legs are distinctly larger than the front legs. There is a nasolabial groove (see Fig. 2) between the nostril and mouth.

SIMILAR SPECIES: An adult, unpatterned Small-mouthed Salamander has a small mouth, has no line from the eye to the corner of the jaw, lacks a sharply keeled tail, and lacks nasolabial grooves.

FOOD: Earthworms, insects, and small crustaceans.

HABITAT: Springs, seeps, creeks, and streams.

REMARKS: The female guards the eggs. This salamander is restricted to the hillsides of the Ouachita Mountain uplift. It is mostly aquatic and could be adversely affected by runoff of pesticides, herbicides, and silt from logging practices. It is nocturnal. Many individuals have visible red mites under the skin of their feet or bodies. This species is rare throughout its range. In Oklahoma, this is a Species of Special Concern and cannot be taken from the wild.

Dark-sided Salamander
Eurycea longicauda melanopleura

Aquatic larva

SIZE: 4-6 inches.

APPEARANCE: The dorsal background color is bright yellow to brownish-yellow with numerous dark spots or blotches down the back. The belly is light gray and may have dark spots. There are dark markings along the sides from the snout to the tail, giving a dark appearance to the sides of the body. Light colored flecks may also be present in the dark area along the sides. The sides of the long tail may be marked with vertical bars, which can fuse together to form an irregular-shaped stripe. The top of the tail is normally yellow with few or no spots. There are 14 costal grooves (see Fig. 1d). Nasolabial grooves (see Fig. 2) are present. Adult males have prominent cirri (see Fig. 2) and females have small cirri.

SIMILAR SPECIES: The Cave Salamander lacks the dark coloration on the sides of the body and is usually orange, not yellow.

FOOD: Small insects, earthworms, and spiders.

HABITAT: Moist woodlands and cave entrances, usually on hillsides.

REMARKS: This salamander is frequently found in cave entrances and fissures in exposed limestone. At night it moves outside of these caves and fissures to feed. Eggs are laid singly attached to rocks in dark areas. The cirri (see Fig. 2) of adults assist in bringing odor molecules to the nasolabial grooves. The name *longicauda* refers to the long tail in this salamander and *melanopleura* means dark sides.

29

Cave Salamander
Eurycea lucifuga

Head showing cirri

SIZE: 4-6 inches.

APPEARANCE: The skin is usually orange but can vary from orange-red to dark yellow. The back and sides are covered with numerous, irregularly spaced black spots or dots that vary in size. It has a long tail, a plain belly that is whitish to yellow, and 13 or 14 costal grooves (see Fig. 1d). There is a nasolabial groove (see Fig. 2). The cirri (see Fig. 2) of an adult male are larger than those of an adult female.

SIMILAR SPECIES: A Dark-sided Salamander has dark coloration along the sides of the body and the dorsal color is usually yellow.

FOOD: Small insects and spiders.

HABITAT: Moist woodlands, cliff fissures, and caves in the limestone regions of northeastern Oklahoma.

REMARKS: Although this salamander is usually found in caves and cliff fissures, it travels outside at night to feed. Adults can also be found in springs and swamps in limestone areas. Larvae live in streams outside of the cave and enter the caves as adults. This adept climber is assisted by its prehensile tail and can jump or leap about the length of its body. Even though this salamander lives in and around caves, it can see quite well. The cirri of adults are important in bringing odor molecules to the nasolabial grooves. The name *lucifuga* translates as flees light, which refers to the fact this species lives in caves. This species is protected by state law and cannot be removed from the wild.

Many-ribbed Salamander
Eurycea multiplicata

Juvenile

SIZE: 2-3 inches.

APPEARANCE: The dorsal color of this small, slender salamander is yellowish to brown and the belly is yellow. There may be a row of V-shaped markings down the middle of the back. Normally, whitish flecks or dots extend along both sides of the body. These salamanders have 19-20 costal grooves (see Fig. 1d). The head is slightly wider than the neck and there is a nasolabial groove (see Fig. 2).

SIMILAR SPECIES: A juvenile Ouachita Dusky Salamander has a light line from the eye to the angle of the jaw. A terrestrial Oklahoma Salamander differs from a Many-ribbed Salamander in its range and the Oklahoma Salamander lacks a yellow belly.

FOOD: Small insects and spiders.

HABITAT: Caves, springs, seeps, creeks, and moist woodlands.

REMARKS: Larvae live in the small spaces among the submerged stream gravel. This species is nocturnal. Recently the Gray-bellied Salamander was shown to be the same as the Oklahoma Salamander, *Eurycea tynerensis*. Therefore, it is no longer a part of this account. The name *multiplicata* refers to the many folds (costal grooves.) The type locality (where the first specimen was discovered) is Choctaw County, Oklahoma near the Red River.

Grotto Salamander
Eurycea spelaea

Terrestrial adult (top) and aquatic larva (bottom)

SIZE: 3-5 inches.

APPEARANCE: The larva has a brown to gray dorsal color with yellow to orange flecking and a distinctly high finned tail. The adult (and larger larva) is pale tan to pinkish in color and may have an orange wash and lightly colored blotches, especially on the tail. Larvae possess external gills, whereas adults do not. Grotto Salamanders have 16 to 19 (usually 17) costal grooves (see Fig. 1d). There is a nasolabial groove (see Fig. 2).

SIMILAR SPECIES: Other adult salamanders have functional eyes and other larvae lack the high finned tail.

FOOD: Aquatic invertebrates and cave insects.

HABITAT: Limestone caves containing water and in adjacent springs and seeps in extreme northeastern Oklahoma.

REMARKS: As an adult, this salamander is blind, has little or no skin color, and long, spindly legs. The aquatic larvae are nocturnal, have functional eyes and may live two to three years outside caves. They are more common than transformed adults. The adults usually reside in caves with a large number of bats. Social bats, such as Gray Bats or Big Brown Bats, leave large piles of guano (bat feces) in caves as they raise their young. The guano piles, rich sources of nutrients, are covered with many species of cave-dwelling invertebrates, which the Grotto Salamander eats. Males have cirri (see Fig. 2) that hang down over the lip during the breeding season. This salamander was previously in the genus *Typhlotriton* but a recent study showed it belonged in the genus *Eurycea*. The name *spelaeus* means cave. This rare salamander is an Oklahoma Species of Special Concern. It is protected by state law and cannot be removed from the wild.

Oklahoma Salamander
Eurycea tynerensis

Aquatic adult (top) and terrestrial adult (bottom)

SIZE: 2-3 inches.

APPEARANCE: The adult may be either aquatic or terrestrial. The aquatic adult may be pale cream to brown-black on the back with dense, dark, gray spotting or stippling; a mix of cream and black on the back with dark markings; varying shades of gray with dark markings on the back; or plain gray. The upper surface of the tail may have a yellow to brown stripe. The aquatic adult has external gills. The terrestrial adult has a brown stripe or v-shaped markings down the back, bordered on each side by a dark brown to black stripe. The belly is gray. This species has a nasolabial groove (see Fig. 2) and 19-21 costal grooves (see Fig. 1d).

SIMILAR SPECIES: A larval Grotto Salamander has a distinct high tail fin and is pink to purplish in color. The Many-ribbed Salamander has a yellow belly.

FOOD: Small aquatic invertebrates.

HABITAT: Cool, clean spring heads and spring fed creeks with thick gravel bottoms.

REMARKS: It needs unpolluted water and is threatened by human practices that deteriorate water quality. Oklahoma Salamanders live in the small spaces among the submerged stream gravel. It is nocturnal. The name *tynerensis* is a reference to Tyner Creek, in Adair County, Oklahoma, which is the type locality (where the first specimen was discovered) of this salamander. Recent research demonstrated that the terrestrial salamanders known as Gray-bellied Salamanders (*Eurycea multiplicata griseogaster*) are Oklahoma Salamanders. Only individuals that remained aquatic as adults were called Oklahoma Salamanders. The Gray-bellied Salamander with terrestrial adults was considered a separate species even though determining whether or not a salamander was an Oklahoma Salamander or a Gray-bellied Salamander was difficult. This uncommon salamander is an Oklahoma Species of Special Concern. It is protected by state law and cannot be removed from the wild.

Four-toed Salamander
Hemidactylium scutatum

Lower animal showing spotted belly

Adult

SIZE: 2-3.5 inches.

APPEARANCE: The dorsal color is reddish-brown to yellowish-brown and the sides are gray. The back and sides are marked with dark spots or flecks. The belly is enamel white with numerous glossy black spots or blotches. There are four toes on the back feet and a constriction at the base of the round tail. Four-toed Salamanders have 12 to 14 costal grooves (see Fig. 1d). There is a nasolabial groove (see Fig. 2).

SIMILAR SPECIES: No other salamander in Oklahoma has a pure white belly with black spots.

FOOD: Small insects, spiders, and earthworms.

HABITAT: Most often found in mossy areas around seeps, spring heads, or ponds in forested areas of extreme southeastern Oklahoma. Sometimes found in more upland wooded habitats.

REMARKS: Nests are usually made under moss along creek or pond banks and the female guards the eggs. When nesting habitat is scarce more than one female will use the same nest. In this case the communal nest is guarded by multiple females. This salamander's tail will readily break at the constriction if it is grabbed by a predator and later the tail can regenerate. This salamander is nocturnal. The genus name *Hemidactylium* refers to the reduced number of toes on the back foot. Most terrestrial salamanders have five toes, rather than four toes, on the back feet. This rare salamander is an Oklahoma Species of Special Concern, is protected by state law, and cannot be removed from the wild.

Western Slimy Salamander
Plethodon albagula

SIZE: 4.5 -7 inches.

APPEARANCE: This is a large salamander with black, dorsal color and whitish or brassy spots or flecks covering the upper body. The white spotting may be heavier along the sides. The amount of spotting varies among individuals and may be very sparse. The plain belly is dark gray to slate colored, and the throat may be slightly lighter than the belly and usually has white spots. It usually has 15 to 17 (commonly 16) costal grooves (see Fig. 1d). It has nasolabial grooves (see Fig. 2).

SIMILAR SPECIES: The Rich Mountain Salamander has a flattened head and a whitish throat. The Kiamichi Slimy Salamander is only on Kiamichi Mountain. The Sequoyah Slimy Salamander is only in the Beavers Bend State Park area.

FOOD: Earthworms, insects, and spiders.

HABITAT: Moist woodlands and caves.

REMARKS: This salamander releases a sticky substance from skin glands when it is disturbed or handled. The black back color with white spots makes this salamander very cryptic when it is under a log or rock. This nocturnal species is territorial and will chase off and bite intruders. The female guards the eggs. This species has direct development. The term *albagula* means white throat. This species was described from the population in central Texas where it has a white throat. In Oklahoma, the throat is not white. This salamander is protected by state law and cannot be removed from the wild.

SALAMANDERS

Ozark Zigzag Salamander
Plethodon angusticlavius

SIZE: 2.25-4 inches.

APPEARANCE: This small, slender salamander has gray to dark brown skin and its sides are covered with small whitish flecks or dots. A narrow mid-dorsal yellow to red stripe extends down the back and onto the tail. This stripe usually has wavy edges and is wider near the base of the tail. Some individuals lack the bright dorsal stripe and are uniformly dark with whitish flecks. The belly is dark and covered with grayish flecks and red pigment. Adults have 17 to 19 (usually 18) costal grooves (see Fig. 1d). This salamander has nasolabial grooves (see Fig. 2).

SIMILAR SPECIES: The Southern Red-backed Salamander lacks red pigment on the belly and has a more irregular-edged, serrated-shaped stripe that is not wider on the tail.

FOOD: Small earthworms, insects, and spiders.

HABITAT: Caves and steep hillsides in moist forested areas.

REMARKS: There are two color types of this salamander, the normal color and the uniformly dark type. Although they look distinctly different, they are both the same species. The female guards the eggs. This species has direct development, a process in which the larval salamander develops within the egg and "hatches" as a miniature adult. This nocturnal species is more tolerant of cold weather than most salamanders in Oklahoma and is active in fall, winter, and spring. Most retreat underground during the summer. Many individuals have a skin infestation of small, red mites, especially on the feet. This salamander is protected by state law and cannot be removed from the wild.

Kiamichi Slimy Salamander
Plethodon kiamichi

SIZE: 4.5-6 inches.

APPEARANCE: It has a black, dorsal color and small whitish or brassy spots or flecks covering the upper body. White to yellow spotting or flecking is normally heavier along the sides of the animal. The amount of spotting varies among individuals and may be sparse in some individuals. The belly is dark gray or slate colored and usually has whitish spots. Adults have 16 to 17 (usually 16) costal grooves (see Fig. 1d). Nasolabial grooves (see Fig. 2) are present.

SIMILAR SPECIES: The Rich Mountain Salamander has a flatter head and a white throat. Neither the Western Slimy Salamander nor the Sequoyah Slimy Salamander is found on Kiamichi or Round Mountain.

FOOD: Earthworms, insects, and spiders.

HABITAT: Moist forested areas on Kiamichi and Round Mountains of LeFlore County.

REMARKS: This species has recently been described and very little is known about its biology or natural history. It is nocturnal. Like the other two slimy salamanders, it secretes a sticky glue-like substance from skin glands when disturbed or handled. It is probably territorial. This species has direct development, a process in which the larval salamander develops within the egg and "hatches" as a miniature adult. The type locality (where the first specimen was discovered) of this species is Round Mountain in LeFlore County, Oklahoma. The name *kiamichi* comes from Kiamichi Mountain, Oklahoma. Because it has such a limited range, this salamander is protected by state law and cannot be removed from the wild.

Rich Mountain Salamander
Plethodon ouachitae

Adult from Rich Mountain

Adult ecomorphs from Kiamichi Mountain (top left), Winding Stair Mountain (top right), and Rich Mountain (bottom center)

SIZE: 4-5 inches.

APPEARANCE: The Rich Mountain Salamander is black and may have light spots on its belly. It has a white throat. There can be dense white pigment on the lateral sides, sometimes forming a continuous band. This salamander exhibits three color forms also known as ecomorphs. On Rich Mountain, the upper body is covered with small white spots and varying amounts of brassy frosting or flecking and chestnut pigmentation. On Winding Stair and Buffalo Mountains, the body is covered with small white spots, some brassy flecking and, rarely, some chestnut pigmentation (especially on the eastern end of Winding Stair Mountain). On Kiamichi Mountain, it is normally black with numerous whitish spots or flecks and no brassy flecks or chestnut pigmentation. The head of the Rich Mountain Salamander is slightly flattened from top to bottom. The Rich Mountain Salamander has 15 to 17 (usually 16) costal grooves (see Fig. 1d). There are nasolabial grooves (see Fig. 2).

SIMILAR SPECIES: A Western Slimy Salamander does not have a flattened head or a completely white throat. On Kiamichi Mountain, a juvenile Rich Mountain Salamander is extremely hard to distinguish from a juvenile Kiamichi Slimy Salamander and can only be distinguished by an expert or by using laboratory techniques to determine genetic differences.

FOOD: Earthworms, insects, and spiders.

HABITAT: Under logs or flat rocks in moist forests mainly on the north-facing talus slopes of the Ouachita Mountains in Leflore, Latimer, and Pushmataha Counties.

REMARKS: This salamander is found in the Ouachita Mountains in southeastern Oklahoma. The species was given the name *ouachitae* because of where it is located. Within its range, it is the most common salamander. However, logging, herbicide, and pesticide use, and other habitat destruction could threaten the existence of this species. In the laboratory, this salamander is territorial and will defend its territory from other Rich Mountain Salamanders and Western Slimy Salamanders. In the field, the same individual can be found under the same cover object from year to year. Laboratory studies have shown that the Rich Mountain Salamander can recognize other Rich Mountain Salamanders by smell. From 60 - 100% of the individuals are visibly infested by small, red mites living in the skin, especially on the feet. It secretes a sticky glue-like substance from skin glands when disturbed or handled. The female guards the eggs and usually breeds biennially. This species has direct development, a process in which the larval salamander develops within the egg and "hatches" as a miniature adult. This salamander is an Oklahoma Species of Special Concern. It is protected by state law and cannot be taken out of the wild.

Adult from Rich Mountain: note mite at tip of tail

Sequoyah Slimy Salamander
Plethodon sequoyah

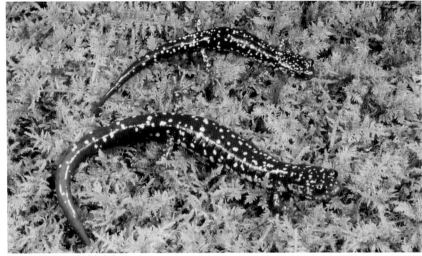

Juvenile (above) and adult (below)

SIZE: 4-5.5 inches.

APPEARANCE: It has a black dorsal color and whitish or brassy spots or flecks covering the upper body. Large white to yellow spots may be heavy along the sides. The amount of spotting varies among individuals and may be sparse. The belly is black to slate colored and may have a few whitish spots. The chin is slightly lighter than the belly and normally has whitish spots. It has 15 or 16 (usually 16) costal grooves (see Fig. 1d). There are nasolabial grooves (see Fig. 2) present.

SIMILAR SPECIES: The Sequoyah Slimy Salamander is the only black slimy salamander with light spots found in the Beavers Bend State Park area.

FOOD: Earthworms, insects, and spiders.

HABITAT: Moist woodlands in the Beavers Bend State Park area of McCurtain County.

REMARKS: This nocturnal salamander is the only amphibian found exclusively in Oklahoma. This species has recently been described and very little is known about its biology or natural history, but it is probably territorial and the female probably guards the eggs. This species has direct development, a process in which the larval salamander develops within the egg and "hatches" as a miniature adult. Like the other two slimy salamanders, it secretes a sticky glue-like substance from skin glands when disturbed or handled. Because it has such a limited range, this salamander is protected by state law and cannot be taken out of the wild. The type locality (where the first specimen was discovered) is Beavers Bend State Park in McCurtain County, Oklahoma.

Southern Red-backed Salamander
Plethodon serratus

Showing both color types: dark (left) and normal (right)

Female guarding eggs

SIZE: 2.5-4 inches.

APPEARANCE: This small, slender salamander is gray to dark brown and the sides of the body are covered with whitish flecks or dots. A red (rarely yellow) stripe with serrated edges extends down the middle of the back and onto the tail. Some individuals lack the red dorsal stripe and are uniformly dark with whitish flecks or dots. The belly is usually dark and covered with grayish flecks and dots. Adults have 18 to 20 (usually 19) costal grooves (see Fig. 1d). There are nasolabial grooves (see Fig. 2).

SIMILAR SPECIES: The Ozark Zigzag Salamander has red pigment on the belly and the dorsal stripe is usually wider on the tail and straight, not serrated.

FOOD: Small earthworms, insects, and spiders.

HABITAT: Moist, rocky forests in the Ouachita Mountains.

REMARKS: There are two color types of this salamander, the normal color (red-backed), and the uniformly dark variation in the Ouachita Mountains (lead-backed). Although these two color forms are obviously distinct, both belong to the same species. The female lays her eggs in a moist location under a log or rock and guards them. The larvae develop within the egg and hatch looking like miniature versions of the adults (called direct development). This species is very tolerant of cool temperatures and can remain active into the late fall and resume activity in early spring. It is usually very difficult to find this nocturnal salamander during the hot summer. This small salamander demonstrates territoriality in laboratory experiments. The name *serratus* means serrated or saw-toothed and refers to the mid-dorsal line. Both color types are pictured.

Frogs and Toads (Order Anura)

BEHAVIOR

Frogs and toads (also called anurans) live in a wide variety of habitats in Oklahoma from the cypress swamps of the southeast to the arid, desert-like regions of the southwest, and high plains of the panhandle. Some are adapted to spend much of their lives underground, while others live in trees or along the banks of rivers and ponds. Anurans are found in nearly every habitat in Oklahoma during some part of the year. Most frogs and toads are encountered around wetlands or crossing roads and driveways at night after or during a rain shower.

Adult anurans prey on a variety of insects, spiders, crustaceans, earthworms, slugs, millipedes, and centipedes. Because of this diet, some gardeners encourage anurans to live in their yards. A single toad can eat thousands of insects and slugs per year. Many toads and frogs take advantage of street lights or other light sources at night and sit under these to catch flying insects. All anurans have a tongue with sticky mucus, which is flipped out to catch prey. Generally only moving insects are eaten. Most larval anurans (tadpoles) eat algae and debris at the bottom of pools and other bodies of water, but some tadpoles prey on aquatic organisms or other tadpoles.

ANATOMY

Adult frogs and toads are easy to distinguish from salamanders because adult frogs and toads have long hind legs, hop or leap, and lack a tail. The name anura indicates that these are the tailless amphibians. Their skin is usually smooth, although in toads it is rough with wart-like glands. Frogs and toads have long toes that are sometimes joined together with skin to form a web that aids in swimming (see Fig. 5). An external ear opening covered by a membrane called a tympanum (eardrum) is visible on either side of the head (see Fig. 3d). Adult frogs and toads can breathe through their skin, but normally rely mostly on the lungs for breathing. In the tadpole stage, however, they respire through gills. Because most tadpoles are herbivorous and adults are carnivorous, numerous changes occur in the digestive tract during metamorphosis. During this time the juvenile does not eat.

The color and pattern of the skin can change with changing environmental conditions. Therefore, to identify an anuran it helps to keep it overnight in a moist container at room temperature. This helps to bring out the pattern and ground color in many species that may become dark and patternless when they are cold.

Many people ask "What is the difference between a frog and a toad?" In a nutshell, nothing. Some people refer to anurans with smooth skin as frogs and rough skinned anurans as toads.

REPRODUCTION

In the spring and early summer, male frogs and toads gather at breeding sites and call to attract females. Each species has its own distinctive call and these calls are often the easiest way herpetologists can identify, locate, and study frogs and toads. Although several different species of frogs and toads may be calling at the same pond, females are attracted only to the calls of males of their own species. Once a male has attracted a female, the male clasps the female's body and fertilizes the eggs as she lays them in the water. Anurans generally lay hundreds to thousands of eggs and a single toad may lay as many as 30,000 eggs. Eggs are usually laid in gelatinous masses or strings. Upon hatching, the tiny larvae (tadpoles) are weak swimmers, making them easy prey for fish, turtles, birds, and water beetles.

Although salamander larvae have visible external gills, the gills of tadpoles are enclosed in a skin-covered chamber. When tadpoles first hatch, they lack legs. The hind legs develop first, with the front legs protruding just before the tadpoles metamorphose into small frogs or toads and leave the water (see Fig. 3). Species vary greatly in the length of time in which they are tadpoles. Some species of spadefoot toads may develop from eggs to tadpoles to juvenile toads in as little as 12 to 15 days. This same process can last two years for Bullfrogs.

CONSERVATION

Since frogs and toads spend part of their lives in water and part on land, they are particularly sensitive to habitat changes. Because their skin is permeable to air and water, it may take up toxins in the air, water, or soil. In recent decades, noticeable declines have been documented in amphibian populations in scattered places throughout the world and therefore we should be alert to changes in our local populations. Small wetlands are especially important for anurans (some cannot breed in the presence of fish). When wetlands are destroyed, long-term species survival is imperiled because most species rely on a network of wetlands so that some can serve as a colonizing source for others.

GROUPS OF FROGS AND TOADS

The genus name *Bufo* means toad. True toads have dry, rough, warty-looking skin and parotoid glands (see Fig. 4) on the head behind the eyes. The large, wart-like parotoid glands secrete a toxic substance that irritates predators attempting to eat a toad. Contrary to popular myth, touching anuran warts (skin glands) or urine cannot give a human warts. Many toads have ridges called cranial crests (see Fig. 4) on their heads. The shape and size of the parotoid glands and the presence or absence and shape of cranial crests are used to identify toads.

Most spadefoots are found in arid to semiarid habitats. The name spadefoot refers to the black, horny spade on the inner side of each hind foot that is used for digging (see Fig. 5d). Spadefoots spend much of the year underground, making only brief appearances above ground to breed in temporary pools. They are nocturnal and their eyes have vertical pupils. Some people show strong allergic reactions when they handle spadefoots.

Narrow-mouthed toads are small, plump, smooth-skinned annurans with triangular-shaped heads with pointed snouts, small mouths, and short, strong, front legs for burrowing. They specialize in eating ants and have a fold of skin behind the head that can be moved forward to sweep away ants that attack the eyes. Some narrow-mouthed toads are found living with tarantulas. Researchers have suggested that the tarantulas protect the narrow-mouthed toads, and they in turn eat ants that can harm the tarantulas.

Treefrogs, chorus frogs, and Cricket Frogs belong to the same group. Treefrogs have large suction cup-like pads on their toes, which are used for climbing (see Fig. 5b). Often they will call from up in trees, hence the name treefrog. If a treefrog is in a dry place, it will adopt a water conserving posture and tuck its legs under its belly. Chorus frogs are small, secretive frogs. They are the first frogs heard calling each spring throughout much of Oklahoma. Cricket Frogs are common on the bare shores of ponds, lakes, and rivers throughout the state. If disturbed, these tiny frogs will jump to safety in the water, but usually swim right back to the shore a little further down the bank.

Oklahoma hosts seven species of true frogs including the largest frog in the United States, the American Bullfrog. Most have smooth skin, webs between the back toes, long muscular legs, and a glandular ridge of skin called a dorsolateral fold on each side of the back (see Fig. 3 and Fig. 5c).

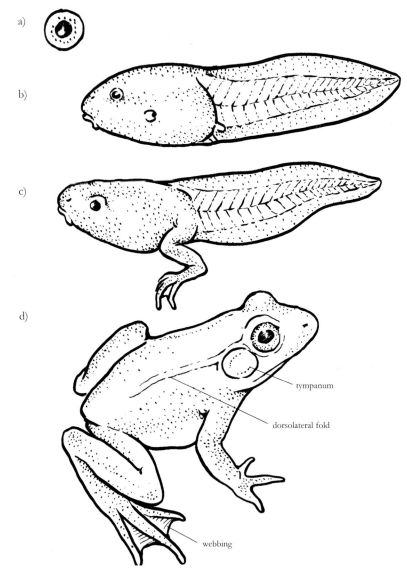

FIG. 3. - General frog life cycle: a) egg; b) tadpole; c) tadpole beginning metamorphosis; d) adult

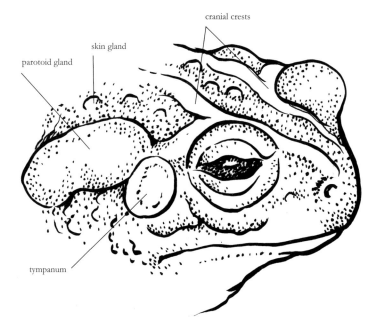

FIG. 4. - Close-up of toad head

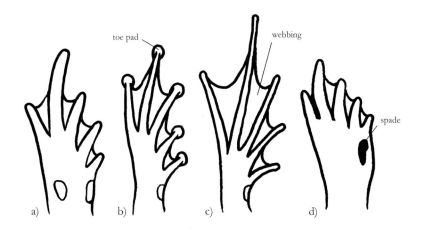

FIG. 5. - Hind feet of frogs and toads: a) toad; b) treefrog; c) frog; d) spadefoot toad

American Toad
Bufo americanus

Adult Dwarf American Toad

Lower animal showing a spotted belly

SIZE: 1.5-3.5 inches.

APPEARANCE: It has a red to brown back with one or sometimes two warts in each obscure dorsal spot. Warts on the back are numerous and small, but warts on the rear lower leg are enlarged and variable in size. Parotoid glands do not touch the cranial crests unless a small spur of the cranial crest extends at a 90-degree angle from the cranial crest to the parotoid gland (see Fig. 4). The belly is mostly light with faint spotting. There are black spades on the hind feet. The Dwarf American Toad is less than 2.5 inches and has a reddish back color. The Eastern American Toad can reach up to 4 inches in length and usually lacks the reddish color on the back.

SIMILAR SPECIES: The Woodhouse's Toad has cranial crests in contact with the parotoid glands and has a plain belly without spotting or has one squarish blotch on the breast. An East Texas Toad is not reddish and has small spiny warts on the leg. A Great Plains Toad has a V-shaped cranial crest.

FOOD: Insects and spiders.

HABITAT: Oak-hickory and pine-oak woodlands, moist prairies, and along river bottoms.

REMARKS: Breeding occurs from mid-February to July in shallow pools of water in woods and prairies. The male calls from the edges of pools and ponds in long, high-pitched trills. Tadpoles sometimes form feeding and metamorphosing aggregations. The tadpole metamorphoses in 28-55 days. A newly metamorphosed toadlet tends to be diurnal, whereas an older adult is nocturnal. This toad is often welcomed into backyards by gardeners because it eats lots of insects. The Dwarf American Toad is sometimes seen sitting under street lights hunting for insects. This subspecies was first described from a pond near Norman, Oklahoma. *Bufo* means toad. Some scientists believe these toads should be in the genus *Anaxyrus* making the scientific names *Anaxyrus americanus americanus* and *Anaxyrus americanus charlesmithi*. See pg. 4.

SUBSPECIES: Dwarf American Toad (*Bufo americanus charlesmith*), eastern Oklahoma except on the higher ridges of the Ouachita Mountains in LeFlore County; Eastern American Toad (*Bufo americanus americanus*), the higher ridges of the Ouachita Mountains in LeFlore County. The taxonomy of this population in Oklahoma has not been resolved.

Eastern American Toads from Ouachita Mountains showing pattern variation

Great Plains Toad
Bufo cognatus

Photos showing color and pattern variation

Calling male

SIZE: 2-4 inches.

APPEARANCE: It has a gray, brown, or greenish-colored back. The back and sides have four to eight large, paired, rounded, dark green, brown, or black blotches. Each blotch is bordered by a light-colored ring. Cranial crests (see Fig. 4) tend to meet and form a prominent V-shaped structure between the eyes with the point of the V near the snout. There is a raised boss on the snout. The parotoid glands are elongated ovals. The belly is pale with little to no spots. There are black spades on the hind feet.

SIMILAR SPECIES: Other *Bufo* do not have cranial crests that meet to form a V-shaped structure between the eyes or a raised boss on the snout.

FOOD: Insects and spiders.

HABITAT: Prairies with sandy or loamy soils.

REMARKS: The Great Plains Toad can be heard calling from March through August when it rains and is warm. Males enter the pools quickly after rains. The male's call is a reverberating, low-pitched, short trill, and a whole chorus of Great Plains Toads can be deafening. This toad is adapted for breeding in buffalo wallows and other shallow, temporary pools that are not excessively muddy. As a consequence of this habitat preference, it is not uncommon for the ponds to dry up before the tadpoles metamorphose. The female may lay two clutches of eggs per year. Large adults are normally encountered in spring before hot weather. In the fall, only juveniles are active. During dry weather, this toad burrows into soil to avoid desiccation. This toad consumes great numbers of cutworms, as well as other insects. This species is nocturnal. *Bufo* means toad. Some scientists believe this toad should be in the genus *Anaxyrus* making the scientific name *Anaxyrus cognatus* (See p. 4).

Color and pattern variation

Green Toad
Bufo debilis

Eastern Green Toad

Western Green Toad

Western Green Toad

SIZE: 1.25-1.75 inches.

APPEARANCE: This is a small, flat toad that has distinctive yellowish to bright green skin with black markings. The skin is roughened by small warts. Large parotoid glands are low, inconspicuous, and much longer than wide (see Fig. 4). Cranial crests are absent or poorly developed. The Western Green Toad has black markings that form a reticulate pattern and the Eastern Green Toad has black markings reduced to tiny spots. Males generally have black or dusky throats, whereas females have yellowish or white throats.

SIMILAR SPECIES: A Green Toad is easily distinguished from all other toads in Oklahoma by its small size and green skin. The Red-spotted Toad may be the same size as a Green Toad, but has round parotoid glands and does not have bright green skin with black markings. A chorus frog lacks warts.

FOOD: Small insects.

HABITAT: Arid, shortgrass-mesquite prairies and shortgrass-juniper woodlands, especially along valleys of small creeks or near fishless ponds.

REMARKS: This is a very secretive, nocturnal species rarely encountered by humans except during the breeding season. It is difficult to find and study because it is very alert, taking refuge under rocks and clumps of grass or flattening its body against the ground when disturbed. Also, its skin color allows it to blend into the surroundings. A few have been observed in southwestern Oklahoma in gypsum caves. Breeding occurs in temporary pools during or after rain. The male will sometimes call along the edges of pools at night and during the day. The call is a short, high-pitched, fast trill, or buzz. Eggs are laid in ponds that frequently dry up; as an adaptation to this kind of habitat, a tadpole metamorphoses when it is less than ½ inch long. *Bufo* means toad. Some scientists believe these toads should be in the genus *Anaxyrus* making the scientific names *Anaxyrus debilis debilis* and *Anaxyrus debilis insidior* (See p. 4).

SUBSPECIES: Western Green Toad (*Bufo debilis insidior*), northwestern corner of Cimarron County; Eastern Green Toad (*Bufo debilis debilis*), southwestern Oklahoma including a disjunct population in the Arbuckle uplift.

FROGS & TOADS

Color variation in Eastern Green Toad

Red-spotted Toad
Bufo punctatus

SIZE: 1.25-2.5 inches.

APPEARANCE: It is Oklahoma's only toad with round or oval-shaped parotoid glands that are no larger than the eye (see Fig. 4). Its back is some shade of pale brown to tan, usually with small red-spotted warts or spots. There are no cranial crests. The belly is white with faint, rounded, dark spots evenly spaced.

SIMILAR SPECIES: A Woodhouse's Toad, Dwarf American Toad, or East Texas Toad has well-developed cranial crests. The Green Toad is small and yellow to green with black markings. A Texas Toad lacks the red spots and is much larger.

FOOD: Small insects, especially ants.

HABITAT: Distribution of this toad is not well understood. Populations are found in rocky areas as well as in shortgrass prairie. It does well in dry habitats.

REMARKS: During the day this nocturnal toad rests beneath flat stones, in rocky crevices, or in mammal burrows. It may also be found in cattle ponds. Unlike the other toads, it seldom burrows into the soil. Most breeding occurs in streams and ponds in late spring to early summer. The male's call is a high-pitched, slow trill. The name *Bufo* means toad and *punctatus* means spotted. Some scientists believe this toad should be in the genus *Anaxyrus* making the scientific name *Anaxyrus punctatus* (See p. 4).

SIZE: 2.5-4 inches.

APPEARANCE: A chubby toad with a back that is olive to gray colored and often quite light with a few large, dark blotches or spots. Cranial crests are lacking entirely or are indistinct. Parotoid glands are small and oval (see Fig. 4). The belly is white with a black spot on the chest. Two black spades for digging are located on the sole of each hind foot, with the inner one being sickle shaped.

SIMILAR SPECIES: The Woodhouse's Toad, Dwarf American Toad, and East Texas Toad have well-developed cranial crests, numerous dark spots on their backs, and their parotoid glands are not oval. An adult Green Toad or Red-spotted Toad is much smaller than an adult Texas Toad.

FOOD: Insects and spiders.

HABITAT: Shortgrass prairies and fields with sandy soil.

REMARKS: It is active at night and feeds along roads, in open fields, and on lawns. Breeding takes place in shallow to intermediate depth pools, ditches, cattle ponds, and along shallow edges of ponds. The male's call is a short, loud, rapidly repeated, high-pitched trill. This is the most abundant toad of southwestern Oklahoma's shortgrass prairie. This toad is well adapted for burrowing. When it is not active, it burrows into the ground to avoid desiccation. *Bufo* means toad and *speciosus* means beautiful. Some scientists believe this toad should be in the genus *Anaxyrus* making the scientific name *Anaxyrus speciosus* (See p. 4).

Woodhouse's Toad

Bufo woodhousii

Note lack of spots on belly

East Texas Toad

Woodhouse's Toad from Cimarron County

Adult Woodhouse's Toad

54

SIZE: 3-4.5 inches.

APPEARANCE: Best identified by eliminating other species, this toad has dark blotches across the back, with each blotch containing two to four wart-like glands within it. Cranial crests are in contact with the parotoid glands (see Fig. 4). There is usually a white to yellow stripe down the middle of the back. The belly is white or yellowish and normally lacks spots. The white breast is often darkened by a single solid black blotch. There are black spades on the hind feet. Warts on the rear lower leg are small and uniform in size. The Woodhouse's Toad has a light tan to dark gray or brown back, often with scattered paired spots. The East Texas Toad has a pale stripe down the middle of the back and paler stripes on each side. It is light tan to gray on the back with small pointed warts (but see below). The legs appear spiny due to numerous, small, pointed warts. The throat is often dark.

SIMILAR SPECIES: A full-grown Woodhouse's Toad is much larger than the other Oklahoma toads. Cranial crests on the Great Plains Toad join to form a V between the eyes, and the cranial crests in the American Toad do not touch the parotoid glands or are connected to it by only a small spur. The American Toad has a spotted belly and the Woodhouse's Toad normally does not.

FOOD: Insects, spiders, and isopods.

HABITAT: Woodhouse's Toads occupy a wide range of habitats including open woodlands, prairies, and the valleys of larger streams and rivers. This is the principal toad of gardens and lawns.

REMARKS: Breeding takes place in various bodies of water from March to August. The call is a high-pitched, shrill "whrrrr" or "waaaah". A newly metamorphosed toadlet is diurnal, but an older adult is nocturnal. This toad is frequently a welcome guest in gardens because it eats many insects. This toad is often observed sitting under street lights hunting for insects. The Woodhouse's Toad burrows into loose soil during the day to avoid desiccation. *Bufo* means toad. Some scientists believe these toads should be in the genus *Anaxyrus* making the scientific names *Anaxyrus woodhousii woodhousii* and *Anaxyrus woodhousii velatus* (See p. 4).

SUBSPECIES: Woodhouse's Toad (*Bufo woodhousii woodhousii*) is common throughout Oklahoma; East Texas Toad (*Bufo woodhousii velatus*) has been reported from sandy areas near water in extreme southeastern Oklahoma although not all herpetologists recognize this as a valid subspecies. Some herpetologists feel that it belongs to the species *Bufo fowleri* and is not a distinct entity. The Woodhouse's Toad from the panhandle of Oklahoma and part of Colorado has been described as a unique subspecies, although most herpetologists do not agree with this. The toad found in the panhandle is larger than most Woodhouse's Toads and has an overall lighter color. Until further work is done on this toad to determine its taxonomic status, it will be considered *Bufo woodhousii woodhousii*.

Tadpole

Couch's Spadefoot
Scaphiopus couchii

Male - note spade on hind foot

Female

SIZE: 2.25-3.5 inches.

APPEARANCE: The back is greenish to yellowish with brown or black mottling or reticulation and it lacks a raised boss between the eyes. The spade on each hind foot is elongate and sickle shaped (see Fig. 5d). During the breeding season, females have a dark reticulate pattern on a lighter greenish ground color while the males may have scattered dark spots on a greenish ground color.

SIMILAR SPECIES: An adult Hurter's Spadefoot or Plains Spadefoot has a raised boss between the eyes. A Plains Spadefoot or New Mexico Spadefoot lacks reticulate green patterns on the back and the spades on the hind feet are wedge-shaped.

FOOD: Insects and spiders.

HABITAT: Shortgrass-mesquite prairie with sandy soil.

REMARKS: This spadefoot breeds at night after rains in temporary waters such as flooded fields and ditches. The call of the male sounds like a high-pitched "yeow" or "baaaaaaaa" bleat of a lamb and is given as the male floats on the water's surface. Eggs are laid in small masses attached to vegetation. Tadpoles can metamorphose in 15 days or less before pools have dried up. When the adult finishes breeding and feeding for the year, it burrows back into the soil and spends the next 10 months or so underground. While it is underground its energy use is reduced by 80% compared to what it uses when it is active on the surface. These adaptations allow Couch's Spadefoot to inhabit arid regions with sandy or porous soils where pools are present for only a short time during the breeding season. In extremely dry years, this toad may not leave its burrow and may spend two years underground. *Scaphiopus* means "shovel foot" in reference to the spade on the foot, which is used for digging.

Elongated spade on the hind foot

SIZE: 2-3.5 inches.

APPEARANCE: The back is green, greenish-brown, or even black and is marked with two pale bands curved in the shape of an hourglass (or reverse parentheses) extending almost the length of the back. There is a raised boss on the head between the eyes. Spades on the hind feet are an elongate sickle shape (see Fig. 5d). The belly is white to pale gray.

SIMILAR SPECIES: The Couch's Spadefoot is smaller, darker green with reticulations, and does not have a raised boss between the eyes. The Plains Spadefoot and New Mexico Spadefoot are smaller, lack the green back, and have wedge-shaped spades.

FOOD: Insects and spiders.

HABITAT: Moist wooded habitats.

REMARKS: This is a secretive, nocturnal species rarely seen except during the breeding season. Breeding occurs in shallow, temporary pools after rains from April through June. The male gives a high-pitched "errrrrrr" call while sprawled on the surface of the water. Tadpoles can form enormous aggregations for feeding and may metamorphose in as little as 12 days after hatching. This adaptation allows Hurter's Spadefoot to inhabit sandy or porous soils where pools are present for only a short time during the breeding season. *Scaphiopus* means "shovel foot" in reference to the spade on the foot, which is used for digging.

Plains Spadefoot
Spea bombifrons

FROGS & TOADS

Several color variations

Tadpole with developing legs

Note the spade on hind foot

SIZE: 1.5-2.5 inches.

APPEARANCE: This highly variable patterned spadefoot has a gray to brown background color. Its back may have scattered red spots, light streaks, and mottling. Adults have a raised boss between or in front of the eyes. The spade on each hind foot is wedge-shaped (see Fig. 5d). The belly is white.

SIMILAR SPECIES: Both the Couch's and New Mexico Spadefoot lack a raised boss between the eyes. A Hurter's Spadefoot has a raised boss behind the eyes, is larger, and has an elongated spade.

FOOD: Insects and spiders.

HABITAT: It prefers sandy or loamy soil in prairie habitats, and river floodplains.

REMARKS: The Plains Spadefoot is active at night especially after rains. This toad may dig down several feet into the soil when it makes a burrow, and may use the same burrow day after day. Breeding starts in March when large numbers of spadefoots gather in temporary pools to breed. The call is a fast, reverberating snore. Eggs hatch and tadpoles quickly metamorphose before the pools dry up. Some tadpoles are cannibalistic while others eat aquatic plants and form aggregations for feeding and protection. The name *Spea* refers to this toad's digging ability and *bombifrons* means lump on forehead in reference to the boss.

New Mexico Spadefoot
Spea multiplicata stagnalis

Note spade on hind foot

Color variation

SIZE: 1.5-2.5 inches.

APPEARANCE: The skin is gray to green with scattered spots and blotches, and this toad lacks a raised boss between or in front of the eyes. The back may have small, reddish warts. The spade on the hind foot is wedge-shaped (see Fig. 5d).

SIMILAR SPECIES: An adult Plains Spadefoot or Hurter's Spadefoot has a raised boss between or in front of the eyes. A Couch's Spadefoot has an elongate spade and is green with a reticulate pattern.

FOOD: Insects and spiders.

HABITAT: Lowlands, flood plains, and playas. Prefers areas of open vegetation and short grass with sandy soil.

REMARKS: Little is known about this spadefoot in Oklahoma. Breeding takes place in quiet areas along streams and in temporary pools. Its call is a long stuttering snore. When handled, this spadefoot emits a secretion that smells like roasted peanuts. Some people react to the skin secretions of this species by developing red, itchy areas on their skin and/or developing watery eyes and nose, and sneezing. This species is nocturnal. *Spea* refers to this toad's digging prowess.

Color variations

SIZE: 0.75-1.3 inches.

APPEARANCE: It has a dark brown to gray back with scattered dark dots, some aligned dorsolaterally. Dark marks and mottling are found on a bluish-white belly. The triangular-shaped head is short with a pointed snout and a small mouth. The skin is smooth and there is a fold of skin behind the eyes. Adult males have a dark throat.

SIMILAR SPECIES: The Great Plains Narrow-mouthed Toad lacks markings on the back, and has a belly that is light with no dark streaks or mottling.

FOOD: Ants, termites, and other small insects.

HABITAT: Heavily wooded flood plains.

REMARKS: Males call from May through July in warm, shallow, well-vegetated pools. Rain stimulates breeding, but sometimes males call whether it rains or not. The call is a short bleating buzz that sounds somewhat like a lamb and does not carry far. The call is similar to the Great Plains Narrow-mouthed Toad, but is lower-pitched. Eggs are attached to vegetation and float as small rafts on the surface. The tadpole has a black back without brassy coloration, fleshy lips, and lacks the black tooth rows found in tadpoles of other genera. This species is nocturnal. It is a good burrower and spends days either in burrows or hiding under moist logs and rocks. *Gastrophryne* literally means belly toad in reference to its pot belly.

Great Plains Narrow-mouthed Toad
Gastrophryne olivacea

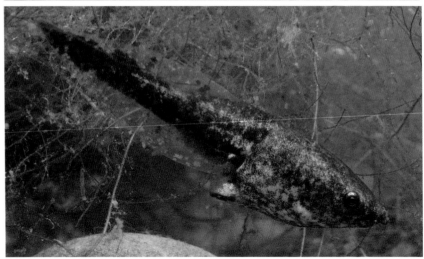

Tadpole

SIZE: 0.75-1.3 inches.

APPEARANCE: It has a gray to dark olive-green or black back with tiny black dots. The belly is light cream to white with no dark spots or mottling. It has a small head, pointed snout, smooth skin, and a fold of skin behind the eyes. Males have a dark throat.

SIMILAR SPECIES: The Eastern Narrow-mouthed Toad's belly is covered with dark marks and mottling.

FOOD: Ants and other small insects.

HABITAT: Prairies, open woodlands, and on dry uplands where rocks abound.

REMARKS: Heavy rains from April through July stimulate it to breed in temporary pools and roadside ditches. The male's call is a short fast trill that sounds like a nasal buzz or high-pitched lamb bleat. The call is similar to that of the Eastern Narrow-mouthed Toad although much higher pitched. It hides beneath rocks and other objects or underground during the day and feeds at night. It is commonly found in occupied tarantula burrows, which may be under rocks or logs and is sometimes called "tarantula toad." As many as 22 toads have been found with a single tarantula under one rock in Wagoner County. The toad benefits by having a home that is safe from predators and the tarantula benefits because the narrow-mouthed toad eats insects (especially ants) that invade the spider's burrow. This species is nocturnal. The tadpole has an olive-brown colored back with small brassy spots, fleshy lips, and lacks the black tooth rows found in tadpoles of other genera. *Gastrophryne* literally means belly toad, a reference to its pot belly, and *olivacea* refers to the olive color of the skin.

Color and pattern variation

Photos showing color variation

SIZE: 1-1.5 inches.

APPEARANCE: This small frog has a dorsal background color that varies from tan, to reddish, to brown with markings that can be shades of black, gray, brown, green, yellow, or red. Light and dark stripes underlie each eye. A triangular-shaped mark is located between the eyes. Light and dark stripes are found on the thighs. The skin on this frog is bumpy, not smooth.

SIMILAR SPECIES: A Boreal Chorus Frog or Cajun Chorus Frog has smooth skin and does not have alternating light and dark bands on the jaw and rear of thigh. Treefrogs are larger and have enlarged toe pads.

FOOD: Beetles, flies, ants, and occasionally isopods and spiders.

HABITAT: Muddy or open banks of permanent or semi-permanent waters.

REMARKS: This species is an excellent swimmer and can skitter across the water on the surface film. It breeds in shallow water from late spring into summer. A Blanchard's Cricket Frog is not strictly nocturnal and can be active during any part of the day or night during spring, summer, and fall. This little frog can often be found sitting at the edge of a pond on sunny, summer days. When approached, it rapidly flees into the water, but usually quickly returns to the bank. This little frog has been observed swimming under ice in the winter. Usually in habitats where there is predation by insect larvae, Blanchard's Cricket Frog tadpoles have a black tail-tip. In habitats where there is heavy predation on these tadpoles by fish, they do not develop the black tail-tip, allowing them to be more cryptic. The male's call is a series of rapid clicks, which sound like glass marbles being repeatedly struck together. *Acris* means locust and comes from the insect-like call of this frog and *crepitans* means rattle.

Tadpole from a fishless pond

Western Bird-voiced Treefrog
Hyla avivoca avivoca

Note the green color on the thighs

SIZE: 1-2 inches.

APPEARANCE: The dorsal color of this frog is gray, green, or brown, and the skin is smooth. The eyes are large. Most individuals have a light-colored spot beneath each eye and darker marks on the back. The inner (hidden) surfaces of the thighs are pale green. The feet have enlarged toe pads (see Fig. 5b).

SIMILAR SPECIES: The Gray Treefrog has a yellow or orange coloration on the inner surface of the thigh and the skin is warty. A typical Spring Peeper has an X-shaped dark mark on the back and is not green.

FOOD: Crawling and flying insects and spiders.

HABITAT: Known only from swamps and roadside ditches near the Little River in McCurtain County.

REMARKS: Males call from late April to mid-July from positions 2 to 8 feet high in the bushes and trees surrounding water. The male's call is a melodious, bird-like trill. It is most active at night, but may call during the day. The tadpole is a very striking animal. It is black with light red blotches on the tail. The species reaches the western limits of its range in southeastern Oklahoma. *Hyla* means of the forest and *avivoca* translates as birdsong. This is an Oklahoma Species of Special Concern and should not be taken from the wild.

Tadpole

SIZE: 1.25-2.25 inches.

APPEARANCE: The dorsal skin is smooth and always green. It has a light, cream-colored stripe extending from the upper lip to the thigh on each side of the body. Shiny, small, golden dots or spots can occur on the back and sides. It has enlarged toe pads (see Fig. 5b).

SIMILAR SPECIES: Chorus frogs and other treefrogs have dark markings on the back and lack a light, cream-colored stripe on the side of the body.

FOOD: Crawling and flying insects.

HABITAT: Swamps, river sloughs, and riparian forests along streams.

REMARKS: Breeding occurs from spring to early summer. Males call while perched above the water in trees, bushes, or cattails. The call sounds like a series of "wank", "wank", "wank", "wank" calls with a metallic cowbell ringing quality. Calling choruses of Green Treefrogs in the Little River National Wildlife Refuge can be deafening to a human listener. This is Oklahoma's largest treefrog. It is nocturnal. The records for Oklahoma, Pottawatomie, and Delaware Counties are probably attributable to frogs that were escaped pets, brought in with potted plants from the southeastern U.S., or misidentified Gray Treefrogs. *Hyla* means of the woods.

Gray Treefrog Complex

Hyla versicolor and Hyla chrysoscelis (Gray Treefrog and Cope's Gray Treefrog)

Color variations in two Cope's Gray Treefrogs

Gray Treefrog (left) and Cope's Gray Treefrog (right)

Gray Treefrog

Cope's Gray Treefrog Tadpole

68

SIZE: 1.25-2 inches.

APPEARANCE: These two species are virtually indistinguishable in appearance. These treefrogs can be light gray to green, although usually they are gray, and have warty-looking skin with irregularly shaped dark markings on the back. The undersides of the thigh are bright orange to yellow and mottled with dark markings. They have enlarged toe pads (see Fig. 5b) and a white spot beneath each eye. Cope's Gray Treefrog is generally the smaller of the two species, usually with a light gray back that can turn completely green. It has less dark mottling on the underside of the thighs than the Gray Treefrog. The adult Gray Treefrog is slightly larger than an adult Cope's Gray Treefrog and varies from gray to mostly green. The author has noticed that the Gray Treefrog cannot become completely green on the back. It will always have black and/or gray lines showing. It has more black markings on the underside of the thighs than the Cope's Gray Treefrog.

SIMILAR SPECIES: The Green Treefrog lacks dark markings on the back and has a light stripe on each side of the body. A Western Bird-voiced Treefrog resembles a Gray Treefrog but the inner surface of the thigh is pale green and the skin is smooth. A Spring Peeper has an X-shaped dark mark on the back.

FOOD: Crawling and flying insects and spiders.

HABITAT: Moist forests and riparian forest along streams.

REMARKS: These species are nocturnal. Breeding occurs from April to July in semi-permanent waters. The male sometimes calls from perches 30 to 60 feet high in trees. A calling male is territorial and will fight intruders. The call of *Hyla versicolor* is a slower, melodious trill and the call of *Hyla chrysoscelis* is a faster grunt-like trill. The call is highly influenced by temperature; the colder the temperature, the slower the trill rate. Calls are more reliable than appearance in identifying these two species in the field. Both species can change colors according to temperature or "mood". In addition, the Gray Treefrogs produce an "antifreeze," which helps prevent them from freezing while hibernating in deep leaf litter. Cope's Gray Treefrog is diploid (has two copies of each chromosome) and has 24 chromosomes. The Gray Treefrog is tetraploid (has four copies of each chromosome) and has 48 chromosomes. The red blood cells of the Gray Treefrog are much larger than the red blood cells of Cope's Gray Treefrog. The tadpole of both species usually has a reddish color on its high-finned tail. *Hyla* means of the woods. The name *versicolor* refers to the variable color (green to gray) and *chrysoscelis* means gold in reference to the gold wash on the thigh.

SPECIES: Gray Treefrog (*Hyla versicolor*) and Cope's Gray Treefrog (*Hyla chrysoscelis*). Because of the difficulty in identifying these two species, the range of each in Oklahoma has not been elucidated. The range map shown here combines the known ranges of both species.

Spotted Chorus Frog
Pseudacris clarkii

Calling male

Adult

SIZE: 0.75-1.5 inches.

APPEARANCE: This is a small slender frog with a gray to brownish-gray back with scattered green spots (rarely stripes) edged with gray to black. A green triangular spot normally occurs between the eyes. The belly is white. During breeding season the male has a dark throat.

SIMILAR SPECIES: A treefrog has enlarged toe pads and extensive webbing between the toes. The Boreal Chorus Frog or Cajun Chorus Frog has three distinct solid stripes on its back. A Spring Peeper has an X-shaped dark mark on the back. A Strecker's Chorus Frog is short, stout, and toad-like with scattered dark marks on the back.

FOOD: Small insects.

HABITAT: Prefers moist areas and seasonally wet lands within tallgrass and mixed prairies. It avoids woodlands and is rare in river flood plains.

REMARKS: It breeds in temporary, flooded, shallow ditches and pools. Most breeding occurs in April and May, but occasionally breeding occurs in October after heavy rains. Males call while hanging onto grass at the water's edge. The call is a fast "reek" "reek" "reek" sound with a metallic quality. Eggs are laid on upright plants in the water. Adults are primarily nocturnal. Outside of the breeding season this frog is hard to find. *Pseudacris* means "false *Acris*".

Mating pair showing male on top

Tadpole, only one front leg has emerged

SIZE: 0.75-1.5 inches.

APPEARANCE: This small frog has a dark brown to gray X-shaped mark on its light-brown back. Often it has a V-shaped dark line between its eyes. The belly is pale and lacks markings.

SIMILAR SPECIES: Other chorus frogs lack the X-shaped mark on the back. A Gray Treefrog, Cope's Gray Treefrog, or Western Bird-voiced Treefrog is larger, has a light spot beneath each eye, and has enlarged toe pads with extensive webbing between the toes.

FOOD: Small insects.

HABITAT: A woodland frog that lives in damp areas with thick vegetation. It is sometimes found in caves.

REMARKS: It breeds from late winter to early spring in temporary to semi-permanent woodland ponds. The call is a series of high-pitched "peep" "peep" "peep" sounds and is considered the harbinger of spring in extreme eastern Oklahoma. Males call from trees, bushes, or cattails standing in or near the water. This frog is nocturnal and rarely seen after the breeding season. The name *Pseudacris* means "false *Acris*" and *crucifer* refers to the cross or X-shaped mark on the frog's back.

Cajun Chorus Frog
Pseudacris fouquettei

FROGS & TOADS

Pattern variant

SIZE: 0.75-1.5 inches.

APPEARANCE: This is a slim, long-legged frog. The dorsal background color is brown with three rows of darker stripes ranging from thick stripes to thin broken stripes. A white line sits above the upper lip. A dark band extends from the snout through the tympanum. The belly is pale with a few dark flecks.

SIMILAR SPECIES: A Boreal Chorus Frog is similarly striped, but has a smaller head, smaller eyes, and shorter legs. The Spring Peeper has an X-shaped mark on the back. Stripes and spots on a Spotted Chorus Frog are green. A Strecker's Chorus Frog has a short, stout, toad-like body with scattered dark spots on the back, but no stripes.

FOOD: Beetles, ants, other insects, and spiders.

HABITAT: Partly wooded areas and prairies.

REMARKS: An adult is rarely found except during the breeding season. This frog often starts calling in the winter when there are warm rains. It breeds during and after heavy rains from March to June. Breeding takes place in shallow bodies of water such as roadside ditches, flooded fields, semi-permanent ponds, and flooded areas near streams. The call is a series of high-pitched notes that sound like a fingernail being run across the teeth of a metal comb. A calling male is difficult to find because it hides in dense, flooded vegetation with only its head above water. Activity is mainly nocturnal, but males call both at night and during the day. Eggs are produced in small, gelatinous packets attached to plants in shallow water. *Pseudacris* means "false *Acris*".

*The Cajun Chorus Frog was described in 2008. It is a cryptic species and hard to distinguish from the Boreal Chorus Frog. The frogs in the Oklahoma range of the Cajun Chorus Frog used to be referred to as the Upland Chorus Frog and the Western Chorus Frog.

Boreal Chorus Frog
Pseudacris maculata

Adult pattern variations

Developing tadpoles

SIZE: 0.75-1.5 inches.

APPEARANCE: It is a slim, small frog. It has three gray to dark brown stripes or lines of dark spots on the lighter background color of the back. There is a pale stripe above the lip and a thicker dark stripe above the pale stripe that extends from the tip of the snout, past the tympanum, and often down the side of the body. The belly is pale with a few small spots.

SIMILAR SPECIES: A Cajun Chorus Frog has a similar back pattern but a larger head, larger eyes, and longer legs. The Spring Peeper has an X-shaped mark on the back. Stripes and spots on a Spotted Chorus Frog are green. A Strecker's Chorus Frog has a short, stout, toad-like body with scattered dark blotches on the back, but no stripes.

FOOD: Beetles, ants, other insects, and spiders.

HABITAT: Partly wooded areas and prairies.

REMARKS: This frog often starts calling in the winter when there are warm rains. It breeds during and after heavy rains from February to June. Breeding takes place in shallow bodies of water such as roadside ditches, flooded fields, semipermanent ponds, and flooded areas near streams. The call is a series of high-pitched notes that sound like a fingernail being run across the teeth of a metal comb. Calling males hide in dense, flooded vegetation with only their heads above water, making them difficult to find. Males call both at night and during the day. Eggs are produced in small, gelatinous packets attached to plants in shallow water. An adult is nocturnal and rarely found except during the breeding season. The name *Pseudacris* means "false *Acris*" and *maculata* means spotted. The frogs in the Oklahoma range of the Boreal Chorus Frog used to be referred to as the Western Chorus Frog.

Pattern variantion

SIZE: 1-1.6 inches.

APPEARANCE: It has short legs and a stout, toad-like body. The back is brown to reddish-brown with scattered dark black or brown blotches. A triangular-shaped blotch is usually present between the eyes. A dark stripe passes from the nose, through the eye, past the shoulder, to the side of the belly. There is a distinct dark spot under each eye. The belly is a pale color.

SIMILAR SPECIES: A treefrog has large toe pads. A Spring Peeper is small usually with an X-shaped dark mark on the back. A Spotted Chorus Frog has scattered green spots on the back and the Cajun Chorus Frog is smaller and typically has three dark stripes on the back.

FOOD: Small insects and spiders.

HABITAT: Distribution closely related to sandy areas in prairies, woodlands, flooded ditches, flood plains, and cultivated fields.

REMARKS: It breeds in late winter and early spring in temporary pools of shallow water and is one of the first frogs to call over much of Oklahoma. The call sounds like a series of high-pitched "ka week" sounds. It burrows and may feed underground. It is nocturnal when it is above ground. It is rarely encountered outside the breeding season. *Pseudacris* means "false *Acris*".

75

Crawfish Frog
Rana areolata

Top two photos showing color variation in Northern Crawfish Frogs

Juvenile Southern Crawfish Frog

SIZE: 2.3-4.75 inches.

APPEARANCE: This frog is stubby with a short, plump body and relatively short legs. It has gray to brown-black dorsal background color with numerous dark spots surrounded by light rings. Light and dark markings between the spots give it a reticulate appearance. The skin on the back is smooth. The dorsolateral folds start behind the eye and extend to the thigh (see Fig. 3d). The belly is white. The subspecies are similar, but the Northern Crawfish Frog is larger, has rougher back skin, a shorter, wider head, and more distinct dorsolateral folds.

SIMILAR SPECIES: A Southern Leopard Frog, Plains Leopard Frog, Pickerel Frog, Northern Green Frog, or American Bullfrog lacks a reticulate appearance of light and dark spots and lines between the spots on the back.

FOOD: Isopods, crickets, beetles, spiders, and possibly crayfish.

HABITAT: Prairies, hay meadows, and woody areas near streams that pass through grasslands.

REMARKS: The adult is secretive, nocturnal and seldom seen except during the breeding season, which is February to April. It is wary and will dive under water if it sees a human. Crawfish Frogs live in crayfish burrows or other abandoned animal burrows. Burrows taken over by a Crawfish Frog have a flattened bare platform at the entrance. This frog breeds in shallow, low-lying, flooded areas with fairly clear water and protruding vegetation. The male's call is a nasal, snore-like "waaah," which he makes from the shore, from shallow water at the pond's edge, or while sprawled on the pond surface. *Rana* means true frog, *areolata* means small light areas between the spots and *circulosa* means full of circles. Some scientists believe this frog should be in the genus *Lithobates* making the scientific names *Lithobates areolatus areolatus* and *Lithobates areolatus circulosus* (See p. 4).

SUBSPECIES: Northern Crawfish Frog (*Rana areolata circulosa*), northeastern Oklahoma; Southern Crawfish Frog (*Rana areolata areolata*), southeastern Oklahoma. The two ranges broadly overlap in east-central Oklahoma, and the subspecies can breed with each other.

Color variation in Juvenile Southern Crawfish Frog

Adult Northern Crawfish Frog

Plains Leopard Frog
Rana blairi

Photos showing color variations

SIZE: 3-4.5 inches.

APPEARANCE: It has conspicuous dorsolateral folds (see Fig. 3d) extending from the eye to the thigh. The folds are broken and inset near the hind end. A distinct white line extends from the snout to just above the arm. The body is tan to reddish-brown with small spots. The skin appears rough. There is usually a dark blotch on the snout and yellow on the insides of the thighs. The belly is white although the groin may be yellow.

SIMILAR SPECIES: The Southern Leopard Frog has a continuous dorsolateral fold, usually no dark spot on the snout, and a more pointed nose. The Crawfish Frog has a reticulate appearance between the spots on the back. The Pickerel Frog has squarish spots arranged in two rows between the dorsolateral folds. A Northern Green Frog or American Bullfrog lacks dark spots on the back and lacks dorsolateral folds that extend to the thigh.

FOOD: Beetles, dragonflies, grasshoppers, worms, and snails.

HABITAT: Temporary and permanent aquatic environments. This is a wide ranging species found about anywhere there is water.

REMARKS: It breeds in early spring and summer in warm, muddy pools, ponds, and ditches. Males call while floating on the surface of the water. Some years this species may also breed in the fall. Youngsters produced in the fall over-winter as tadpoles. The call is a series of "chuck" "chuck" "chuck" "chuck" sounds and at other times it may sound like fingers being rubbed across a taut balloon. This species may hybridize with Southern Leopard Frogs where their ranges overlap. It is mainly nocturnal, but may be observed jumping into a pond when approached on a summer day. On rainy summer nights this frog can often be found. The name *Rana* means true frog. Some scientists believe this frog should be in the genus *Lithobates* making the scientific name *Lithobates blairi* (See p. 4).

Tadpole

FROGS & TOADS

Adult

Adult male and juvenile

Close-up of male

80

SIZE: 4-7 inches.

APPEARANCE: The largest frog in Oklahoma. It has no dorsolateral folds (see Fig. 3d), but it has a fold of skin running from behind the eye around the back edge of the tympanum. The back and sides are green to brown and dark bands are visible on the hind legs. The tympanum in males is larger than the eye whereas the tympanum in females is the same size or smaller than the eye. During the breeding season the throat of the male is bright yellow.

SIMILAR SPECIES: All other true frogs (*Rana*) have dorsolateral folds extending down the sides past the tympanum.

FOOD: Crayfish, insects, frogs, reptiles, mice, and birds. Basically anything that will fit in its mouth.

HABITAT: Found statewide near streams, rivers, ponds, lakes, swamps, and caves.

REMARKS: Primarily active at night, but does bask in the sun during the day. It moves at night during and after rains from one body of water to another. The adult can be found all year except during winter. Breeding occurs from late spring to early summer and some males call into the fall. The call sounds like a series of deep "ha woom" sounds. A single female can lay up to 40,000 eggs. This is one of the last frogs to breed in Oklahoma. In the winter, an American Bullfrog spends its time in shallow water frequently moving from one spot to another within the pond. In captivity this frog will readily eat smaller frogs and should not be housed with smaller animals. The tadpole has very distinctive black spots scattered over the body and obtains a larger size than tadpoles of other species. The record size for an Oklahoma American Bullfrog is 8 inches snout-vent length and 2 pounds in mass. The American Bullfrog is a game species and subject to bag limits. This species has been introduced into the western parts of the United States where it has been outcompeting the native frog species. In these areas it is has become an introduced pest that is difficult to eradicate. The name *Rana* means true frog.

Some scientists believe this frog should be in the genus *Lithobates* making the scientific name *Lithobates catesbeianus* (See p. 4).

Tadpole

Green Frog
Rana clamitans

Adult male Northern Green Frog

Adult female Bronze Frog

Male Bronze Frog

SIZE: 2.5-3.5 inches.

APPEARANCE: It has a brown to green body with dorsolateral folds (see Fig. 3d) that peter out and do not reach further than halfway to the thigh. A pale line extends from below the eye to the arm. There may be a greenish wash below and anterior to the eye. A few bumps, faint spots or dark blotches may occur on the back, sides, or legs. The belly is white with dark, worm-like markings. The throat of breeding males is yellow. The tympanum of the male is larger than the eye. In the female, the tympanum is the same size or smaller than the eye. The Bronze Frog is bronzy colored, often with a green cast around the lips. The Northern Green Frog is brown or green with obvious dark markings on the back.

SIMILAR SPECIES: A Southern Leopard Frog, Plains Leopard Frog, Pickerel Frog, or Crawfish Frog has prominent dark spots on the back. The American Bullfrog lacks the dorsolateral fold extending halfway to the thigh.

FOOD: Insects and spiders.

HABITAT: Edges of rivers, small streams, swamps, and ponds in bottomland forests. Occasionally found along fast-flowing streams and in springs and caves in the Ozarks. It is never found far from permanent water.

REMARKS: It breeds from May through July. The male establishes a territory and will wrestle with other males who invade his territory. The call sounds like the plucking of a loose banjo string. This frog is solitary, nocturnal, secretive, and difficult to approach. The name *Rana* means true frog, *clamitans* refers to loud calling, and *melanota* means marked in black (the dark markings). Some scientists believe this frog should be in the genus *Lithobates* making the scientific names *Lithobates clamitans clamitans* and *Lithobates clamitans melanotus* (See p. 4).

SUBSPECIES: Northern Green Frog (*Rana clamitans melanota*), northeastern Oklahoma westward to Lincoln County; Bronze Frog (*Rana clamitans clamitans*), southeastern Oklahoma westward to Johnston County. The two subspecies can breed with each other where their ranges overlap.

Adult female Northern Green Frog

Pickerel Frog
Rana palustris

SIZE: 1.5-2.3 inches.

APPEARANCE: It has rectangular or squarish spots arranged in two rows between the dorsolateral folds (see Fig. 3d). There are two rows of spots lateral to the dorsolateral folds. A white line extends from the snout to above the arm. The line is thickest anterior to the eye. The underside of the hind legs and groin region is yellow to golden color. The belly is pale white and some individuals have faint mottling on the belly.

SIMILAR SPECIES: A Southern Leopard Frog, Plains Leopard Frog, or Crawfish Frog does not have squarish to rectangular shaped spots in two rows between the dorsolateral folds or yellow coloring on the groin region or the underside of the hind legs.

FOOD: Insects and spiders.

HABITAT: Wet meadows, woodland ponds, small streams, and around cave entrances.

REMARKS: Two disjunct populations of Pickerel Frogs occur in Oklahoma, one in the southeast and the other in the Ozarks. During winter this species may form aggregations under rocks near the mouths of springs or caves in the Ozarks. The skin secretions are toxic and may irritate or even kill other animals kept in the same container with it. Most frog-eating predators will not eat Pickerel Frogs. It breeds from late April to mid May in ponds, along quiet stream edges, and in ditches. The call of the male sounds like a short descending snore sound. This frog is nocturnal. The name *Rana* means true frog and *palustris* means marsh dweller. Some scientists believe this frog should be in the genus *Lithobates* making the scientific name *Lithobates palustris* (See p. 4).

Photos showing color variations in adults

SIZE: 2-3.5 inches.

APPEARANCE: It has a continuous dorsolateral fold (see Fig. 3d) that extends from the eye to the thigh. A distinct white line extends from the snout to just behind the arm. The dorsal color is brown with some green. Usually it lacks a dark blotch or spot on the snout. The snout is pointed. The spots on the back are small to medium sized. The skin is relatively smooth. The belly is pale.

SIMILAR SPECIES: The Plains Leopard Frog has a broken, inset dorsolateral fold at the hind end and a spot on the snout. The Crawfish Frog has a reticulate appearance between the dorsal spots. The Pickerel Frog has squarish spots arranged in two rows between the dorsolateral folds. The Northern Green Frog, Bronze Frog, or the American Bullfrog lacks the dorsolateral fold that extends to the thigh.

FOOD: Isopods, spiders, beetles, grasshoppers, and small crayfish.

HABITAT: Lakes, ponds, rivers, streams, swamps, and sloughs.

REMARKS: It breeds in fall, winter, and early spring in cooler, clearer streams, pools, and ponds. The male calls from the banks or while submerged in the water. The call is a rapid "chuck-chuck-chuck" that almost sounds like the frog is chuckling. The call often ends with a sound similar to fingers being run over a taut balloon. This species may hybridize with Plain Leopard Frogs where their ranges overlap. This nocturnal frog is active some distance from the water during and after rains and is sometimes found on lawns and in gardens during the summer. The name *Rana* means true frog. Some scientists believe this frog should be in the genus *Lithobates* making the scientific name *Lithobates sphenocephalus utricularius* (See p. 4).

Wood Frog
Rana sylvatica

SIZE: 1.4 - 2.75"

APPEARANCE: It has uninterrupted dorsolateral folds that start just behind the eye and extend to the thigh (see Fig. 3d). It has variable background color, but always has a distinct large brown mask from the snout to behind the tympanum above the upper lip. A white line sits above the upper lip extending from the snout to the posterior edge of the mask. The eye is larger than the tympanum. The belly is white with some markings possible. The hind legs may have dark bars.

SIMILAR SPECIES: No other large frog has the brown mask on its face. Strecker's Chorus Frog is much smaller.

FOOD: Insects and spiders.

HABITAT: Ozark area near the Arkansas border in Adair County. It lives in moist woodlands or in caves.

REMARKS: This species was first discovered in the state in 1999 inside a cave. It breeds in February and March in small ponds. It is an explosive breeder and is in the ponds and calling only for a short period of time. The call is a high-pitched, laugh-like chuckle. A whole chorus may sound like a group of quacking ducks. Although it is active for most of the year, it is nocturnal, secretive, and hard to find. The name *Rana* means true frog and *sylvatica* refers to woods or forest. Some scientists believe this frog should be in the genus *Lithobates* making the scientific name *Lithobates sylvaticus* (See p. 4).

REPTILES

SIZE: 6-16 feet.

APPEARANCE: This semi-aquatic reptile has four legs and a long thick tail.

SIMILAR SPECIES: A released non-native caiman has a curved, bony ridge in front of the eye.

FOOD: Fish, mammals, birds, turtles, snakes, frogs, and invertebrates.

HABITAT: In or near permanent sources of water such as rivers, swamps, sloughs, or sluggish streams. It is infrequently seen in the coastal plain region of the Red River and its backwaters especially in extreme southeastern Oklahoma.

REMARKS: Sightings of American Alligators in Oklahoma are rare and some of them can be traced to individuals released in McCurtain County. During the winter it digs deep holes or dens in which to hibernate. During the spring breeding season, the male attracts a female by emitting loud bellows and ultrasonic vibrations into the water. This species and the introduced Turkish House Gecko are the only reptiles in Oklahoma with a voice. Alligators have temperature dependent sex determination. The American Alligator gives more parental care to its young than any other Oklahoma reptile. The mother builds a large cavity, deposits her eggs, and fills the nest with vegetation. As the vegetation rots, it gives off heat and warms the eggs. Young start to make noise just before hatching. The mother hears the young and helps them get from the nest to the water. The young then stay with the parent for about a year. Anecdotal information indicates that the Oklahoma population may be increasing in number. Hard-shelled turtles living in the vicinity of alligators often show scars from encounters with the alligators. In some states the American Alligator is raised for its meat and hide. *Alligator* comes from a Spanish word for lizard. The American Alligator is an Oklahoma Species of Special Concern. It is protected by state law and cannot be removed from the wild.

Turtles

BEHAVIOR

Turtles are relatively inoffensive and bite only when pestered or handled. Most will hide when approached and spend the majority of their time basking, sleeping, and searching for food. Most species are diurnal, but a few are nocturnal. With the exception of the two species of box turtles, all of Oklahoma's turtle species are found in or near water.

Even when basking, aquatic turtles are alert and will readily jump into water if they feel threatened. Like other reptiles, a turtle's ability to respond to stimuli is temperature dependent and at warmer temperatures they can move and digest food more quickly than at colder temperatures. Turtles are most active from spring through the fall and during the winter they burrow into the ground or remain motionless or sluggish on the bottom of a lake or river and stay there until the weather warms. Occasionally turtles may be seen moving about at the bottom of an ice covered pond in winter.

ANATOMY

All turtles have a shell that serves as a protective cover. Turtle shells are covered with large scales, called scutes, which vary in size and shape and can be used to identify some species. The turtle's ribs and backbone form a part of the carapace (upper portion of the shell), therefore, contrary to popular myth, a turtle cannot separate itself from its shell. Box turtles have a hinged plastron (hard plate under the body forming the lower portion of the shell), which allows the shell to close tightly (see Fig. 6b) so they can pull their head and legs inside for protection. Turtles have well developed senses of hearing and vision. Though they lack teeth, turtles have a beak, which is used for biting their food. Male turtles normally have thicker, longer tails than females of the same species. In the turtle accounts, adult size is given as a straight-line measurement of the carapace length.

REPRODUCTION

Most turtles engage in courtship prior to mating in the spring. Eggs are laid in early summer in a nest dug in damp soil by the female. Female turtles dig a small chamber in the ground with their back legs, deposit their eggs, and cover the chamber with soil. The young of many species hatch in late summer or fall and dig their way out of the nest cavity, whereas others remain in the nest until the following spring. Even though some of our turtles spend most of their time in water, their eggs have to be laid on land. Eggshells are permeable and the eggs would fill with water and the developing embryos would drown if they were laid in water. Females do not incubate eggs or care for young. In Oklahoma, young turtles range from ¾ of an inch to two inches in length at hatching. Young often inhabit mats of algae or other aquatic vegetation at a pond's surface and may be difficult to observe. With the exception of the softshell turtles, all of Oklahoma's turtles have temperature dependent sex determination in which the sex of the hatchling turtle depends on the temperature of the nest during incubation.

LONGEVITY

Turtles can live to be quite old. Records indicate that some species found in our area can live to be 75 to 100 years old.

CONSERVATION

Many basking sliders and cooters are needlessly killed because people believe they are eating the fish in the pond. Adult sliders and cooters are chiefly vegetarians and eat only aquatic plants that is often overgrown. Normally these turtles eat only sick, injured, or dead fish.

Cars kill a number of box turtles and aquatic turtles that are traveling from one pond to another or that are leaving the pond to lay eggs. Other factors that affect turtle populations include habitat loss and pesticides/herbicides that reduce the turtles' food supplies or have the potential to injure turtles. Another cause for concern is commercial harvest for the pet trade or for food or medicinal uses, principally in overseas markets.

GROUPS OF TURTLES

Oklahoma has four groups of turtles. The snapping turtles are our largest turtles and have large heads and long tails. They have the most threatening display behavior of all the turtles in Oklahoma, although none of our turtles are aggressive to humans unless provoked.

The second group includes the small-to-medium sized musk and mud turtles. When captured or handled, these turtles often emit a foul smelling musk, hence the names Stinkpot and musk turtle. Some will bask while resting in shallow water with only part of the carapace exposed. Musk turtles have a hinge in the front portion of the plastron, whereas the mud turtles have a hinge in both the front and back portions of the plastron (see Figs. 8a and 8b). The tails of these turtles are much shorter than those of snapping turtles.

The familiar aquatic turtles and the box turtles are small-to-medium sized and, except for the box turtles, have low shells. These species are frequently found basking above the water on logs and rocks or near the water's edge. There is a tendency for the young to be carnivorous and the adults to be omnivorous or herbivorous. Males of some aquatic species have long, curved claws on the front feet that are used to stimulate females during courtship.

The softshell turtles are flat and have soft, leathery shells that lack scutes. Softshell turtles are good swimmers and can move quite rapidly on land as well as in water. Although they may leave the water to bask, softshells stay close to water and are able to retreat quickly if threatened. Frequently these turtles bury themselves in sand along the bottom of streams.

TURTLES

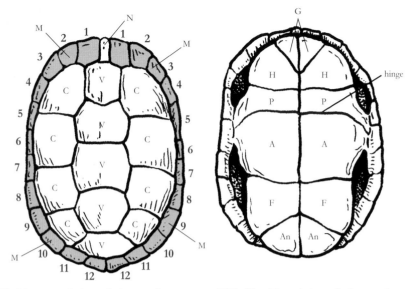

FIG. 6A. - Dorsal view of a box turtle carapace. Scutes (scales) of the shell are: N = nuchal; V = vertebral; C = costal; M = marginal (shaded scutes). The marginal scutes on this figure are numbered

FIG. 6B. - Ventral view of a box turtle plastron. Scutes (scales) of the shell are: G = gular; H = humeral; P = pectoral; A = abdominal; F = femoral; An = anal

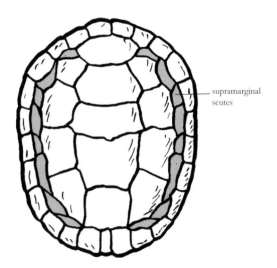

FIG. 7. - Generalized view of a turtle carapace showing supramarginal scutes (shaded scales)

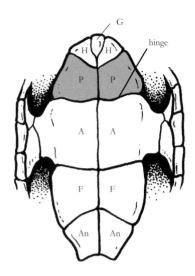

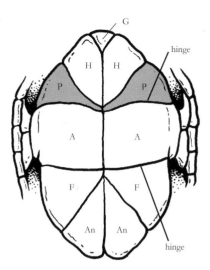

FIG. 8A. - Ventral view of musk turtle plastron showing single hinge in front of the abdominal scute. Note rectangular pectoral scutes. Scutes (scales) of the shell are: G = gular; H = humeral; P = pectoral; A = abdominal; F = femoral; An = anal

FIG. 8B. - Ventral view of mud turtle plastron showing hinges on the front and back of the abdominal scutes. Note triangular pectoral scutes. Scutes (scales) of the shell are: G = gular; H = humeral; P = pectoral; A = abdominal; F = femoral; An = anal

Eastern Snapping Turtle
Chelydra serpentina serpentina

Hatchling

SIZE: 8 – 18.5 inches.

APPEARANCE: The carapace varies in color from black to light brown. Young snapping turtles have three prominent, saw-toothed keels along the top of the carapace, but these become less obvious as the turtle ages. The adult head is large and plastron is small with 9 scutes. The skin is gray to black or yellow. There are barbels at the tip of the chin. The tail is long with a saw-toothed upper edge. The neck and tail are each as long as the carapace. This turtle is often covered with algae. Adult males are usually larger than adult females.

SIMILAR SPECIES: The Alligator Snapping Turtle lacks or has reduced saw-toothed projections on the tail and has a neck shorter than the carapace. Also, it has supramarginal scales (see Fig. 7) and plates on top of the head and the Eastern Snapping Turtle does not. Mud and musk turtles lack three keels on the carapace and have a larger plastron.

FOOD: Carrion, plant material, aquatic invertebrates, fish, reptiles, birds, and mammals.

HABITAT: Fresh water, preferably with a mud bottom and abundant vegetation.

REMARKS: An adult can inflict a nasty bite or emit an odoriferous musk if bothered. Maximum weight for this species is around 85 pounds. Most of the time this nocturnal turtle is found under water, or it may sit in shallow water with only the nostrils exposed to air. It will occasionally leave water and travel on land. Sometimes it will hide under debris in the water or in muskrat burrows. Picking up an Eastern Snapping Turtle by the tail can result in injury to the turtle. This species exhibits temperature dependent sex determination. Although reputed to kill game birds and fish, this is a rare occurrence and normally only sick or injured animals are taken. This culling can improve the quality of the fish population. The scientific name *Chelydra serpentina* means snake-like turtle.

94

Alligator Snapping Turtle
Macrochelys temminckii

Hatchling

SIZE: 15-26 inches.

APPEARANCE: This, our largest turtle, has a hooked beak, a long, smooth tail, and a small plastron with 9 scutes. Three prominent keels on the carapace persist through adulthood. The carapace has supramarginal scales (see Fig. 7) and is often covered in algae. It has a large head, which cannot completely retract into the shell, and barbels at the tip of the chin. The top of the head has plates and the upper jaw sticks out beyond the lower jaw. There is a worm-like pink process on the floor of the mouth that when wiggled lures fish into the turtle's mouth. In Oklahoma, because of past capture of large individuals and lack of sufficient time for growth of smaller individuals, sexual dimorphism in adult size is not always apparent.

SIMILAR SPECIES: The tail of the Eastern Snapping Turtle has a saw-toothed upper edge, and the carapace of an adult lacks the prominent ridges and supramarginal scales.

FOOD: Eats anything it can capture: especially aquatic invertebrates, fish, and other turtles.

HABITAT: Lakes, rivers (especially right below dams), oxbows, and sloughs. It particularly likes canopy covered areas.

REMARKS: It is nocturnal and seldom basks. The Alligator Snapping Turtle prefers deeper water than the Eastern Snapping Turtle, especially during extremes in temperature. Only females regularly leave the water and only to lay eggs. Adults can attain weights of over 250 pounds. In Oklahoma this species takes 10 - 20 years to attain sexual maturity. It can emit a nasty-smelling musk if bothered. The Alligator Snapping Turtle has experienced a drastic range reduction in Oklahoma in recent decades. It is sometimes eaten by humans. This species has temperature dependent sex determination. *Macrochelys* means big turtle. This turtle is an Oklahoma Species of Special Concern. It is protected by state law and cannot be removed from the wild.

SIZE: 3.5-5 inches.

APPEARANCE: The carapace varies from yellow to brown and is often flattened on top. The head lacks markings and the chin and throat are yellow. The jaw is hooked. There are barbels on the chin. The 9th marginal scute on the carapace sticks up higher than others. The male has an area of rough scales on the back legs. Its double-hinged plastron has dark borders on yellow to brown scutes. The pectoral scutes on the plastron are triangular (see Fig. 8b) and there is a single gular scute for total of 11 scutes on the plastron. Adult males are larger than adult females. Hatchlings have black dots at the posterior edge of the carapace scutes.

SIMILAR SPECIES: The Mississippi Mud Turtle does not have a yellow chin or throat and does not have an elevated ninth marginal scute. The Razor-backed Musk Turtle or a Stinkpot lacks a double-hinged plastron and has a rectangular pectoral scute.

FOOD: Insects, mollusks, crustaceans, amphibians, carrion, and aquatic plants.

HABITAT: Slow moving water with a soft, muddy bottom, lakes, ponds, and water filled ditches. Although mainly aquatic, the Yellow Mud Turtle frequently comes onto land and may even feed on land.

REMARKS: The Yellow Mud Turtle can be found in shallow, temporarily flooded pools in the soft mud and can be located by feeling in the mud. Like other mud and musk turtles it can expel a foul musk if irritated. This species has temperature dependent sex determination. This species is inactive for much of the year. It frequently estivates during the hot, dry parts of the summer after its ponds have dried up, then lies dormant, buried in the soil, until the following spring. The name *Kinosternon* means movable chest in reference to the hinged plastron and *flavescens* means yellow.

Mississippi Mud Turtle
Kinosternon subrubrum hippocrepis

Underside/plastron

SIZE: 3-4.75 inches.

APPEARANCE: This species is characterized by two yellowish lines, which may be broken, along the side of a dark gray head. The oval carapace ranges in color from olive to brown. It has a double-hinged plastron with a single gular scute, yielding a total of 11 scutes on the plastron. The pectoral scutes of the plastron are triangular (see Fig. 8b). The head, tail, and carapace of adult males are larger than those of females, but females have a longer plastron than males. Males have two areas of rough, tilted scales on the back legs.

SIMILAR SPECIES: The Yellow Mud Turtle has a yellow chin and throat. The Razor-backed Musk Turtle or a Stinkpot has a single hinge on the plastron and has rectangular pectoral scutes.

FOOD: Insects, crustaceans, mollusks, amphibians, carrion, and aquatic plants.

HABITAT: Slow moving water and swamps with a muddy bottom and abundant aquatic plant life. May live in muskrat burrows.

REMARKS: This turtle is mainly aquatic, but will venture onto land, especially in the morning or evening. This species is frequently seen crossing roads in May and June. The musk of this species is less pungent than that of the musk and snapping turtles. This turtle has temperature dependent sex determination. The name *Kinosternon* means movable chest, referring to the hinged plastron, and *subrubrum* refers to the juvenile's red plastron.

Razor-backed Musk Turtle
Sternotherus carinatus

Carapace color variations

SIZE: 4-5 inches.

APPEARANCE: This turtle has a small, steeply sloped carapace with a distinct ridge along the midline. Barbels occur only on the chin. The jaws are tan and the skin is brown to gray. There is a single hinge on the plastron, which may be difficult to see. There is usually not a gular scute on the plastron, resulting in a total of 10 plastral scutes. The pectoral scutes on the plastron are rectangular (see Fig. 8a). The skin shows between the plastral scutes. Males have an area of rough, tilted scales on the back legs and a blunt spine on the end of the tail. The shell height is about ½ of the shell width.

SIMILAR SPECIES: The Yellow Mud Turtle and Mississippi Mud Turtle have a double-hinged plastron, triangular-shaped pectoral scutes, and a gular scute on the plastron, giving a total of 11 plastral scutes. An adult Stinkpot lacks the ridge along the midline of the carapace and has a gular scute, two light lines on each side of the head, and barbels on the throat as well as on the chin.

FOOD: Invertebrates, amphibians, carrion, and aquatic plants.

HABITAT: Moving water with gravel bottoms.

REMARKS: This turtle feeds at the bottom of streams or creeks. It basks more than Stinkpots and has been observed basking in fallen trees six feet above the water. If startled it will fall into the water. It is active during the afternoon into evening and again from pre-dawn through morning. If bothered it can excrete a pungent musk. This species has temperature dependent sex determination. *Sternotherus* means hinged chest and *carinatus* refers to the keeled midline of the carapace.

Stinkpot
Sternotherus odoratus

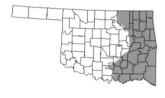

Hatchling

SIZE: 3-4.5 inches.

APPEARANCE: This turtle has a low, rounded, dark carapace. Two light-colored lines run along each side of the head and barbels can be found on the chin and throat. The single hinge on the plastron may be difficult to see. There is one gular scute on the plastron, giving a total of 11 scutes on the plastron. The pectoral scute on the plastron is rectangular (see Fig. 8a). The skin can be seen between the scutes of the plastron, but this is more obvious in males. The male has an area of rough, tilted scales on the back legs and a blunt tail with a claw-like end. This turtle is often covered with algae.

SIMILAR SPECIES: The Yellow Mud Turtle and Mississippi Mud Turtle have a double-hinged plastron and a triangular pectoral scute. The Razor-backed Musk Turtle has 10 plastral scutes, lacks the two light lines on the face, and has a ridge extending down the midline of the carapace.

FOOD: A wide variety of plants and animals.

HABITAT: Quiet, shallow or muddy-bottomed aquatic habitats.

REMARKS: A Stinkpot rarely leaves the water and is seldom seen even where abundant. It normally walks under water and is not a strong swimmer. Its activity is nocturnal. It usually does not bask, but it may sit in shallow water with its back exposed or climb onto the branches of bushes or small trees overhanging the water. This species has temperature dependent sex determination. *Sternotherus* means hinged chest. The term *odoratus* refers to the smell of the musk this turtle releases.

TURTLES

Southern Painted Turtle
Chrysemys dorsalis

Hatchling

SIZE: 4-7 inches.

APPEARANCE: The carapace is smooth and olive to black with a yellow, orange, or red stripe down the middle. The posterior edge of the carapace is not serrated. The plastron lacks hinges. The skin is dark green to black with yellow to red lines on the legs and neck. Females are larger and have shorter tails than males. The plastron is plain yellow.

SIMILAR SPECIES: No other aquatic turtles in Oklahoma have a yellow or red stripe on the carapace. The Western Painted Turtle grows larger, has a more intricate shell pattern, and has red on the plastron.

FOOD: Young are carnivorous and adults are omnivorous.

HABITAT: Lakes, ponds, marshes, and rivers.

REMARKS: The Southern Painted Turtle basks during the day on logs, rocks, and by the water's edge. It can frequently be found traveling over land in search of new habitat or egg laying sites. If the eggs are laid late in the year the young may overwinter in the nest as eggs or hatchlings. The male has long front claws, which are used for courting females. The male will orient himself so that he is facing the female and then stretch his forelegs forward and tap his claws on the female's head. This species has temperature dependent sex determination. The name *Chrysemys* refers to the golden plastron. The Western and Southern Painted Turtles were considered subspecies of a single species until a recent taxonomic paper elevated the Southern Painted Turtle to a separate species.

Western Painted Turtle
Chrysemys picta bellii

Plastron

SIZE: 4-7 inches.

APPEARANCE: The carapace is smooth and olive to black with a yellow to red reticulate pattern of lines. There are light or red vertical bars on the marginal scutes and red on the shell and body. The posterior edge of the carapace is not serrated. The plastron lacks hinges and is plain yellow to orangish around the edge with a dark mottled region in the center. The skin is dark green to black with yellow to red lines on the legs and neck. Females are larger and have shorter tails than males.

SIMILAR SPECIES: Other aquatic turtles in Oklahoma lack numerous red lines on the carapace. The Southern Painted Turtle has a less intricate shell pattern and a yellow plastron.

FOOD: Young are carnivorous and adults are omnivorous.

HABITAT: Lakes, ponds, marshes, and rivers.

REMARKS: The Western Painted Turtle basks during the day on logs, rocks, and by the water's edge. It can frequently be found traveling over land in search of new habitat or egg laying sites. If the eggs are laid late in the year the young may overwinter in the nest as eggs or hatchlings. The Western Painted Turtle is one of the first turtles to become active in the spring, even when ice is still on the pond. The male has long front claws, which are used for courting females. The male will orient himself so that he is facing the female and then stretch his forelegs forward and tap his claws on the female's head. This species has temperature dependent sex determination. The name *Chrysemys* refers to the golden plastron and *picta* means painted in reference to the intricate pattern on the plastron. The Southern and Western Painted Turtles were considered subspecies of a single species until a recent taxonomic paper elevated the Southern Painted Turtle to a separate species.

Western Chicken Turtle
Deirochelys reticularia miaria

Note the vertical yellow stripes on the hind legs

SIZE: 4-10 inches.

APPEARANCE: It has an oval or pear-shaped tan to olive carapace with a network of yellow lines. The head is green with yellow stripes and the neck and head are about as long as the plastron. The front legs are dark with yellow stripes running down them. On the front of the forelegs, the yellow stripe is much broader. The hind legs have vertical yellow stripes (giving the appearance of striped pants). The plastron is yellow and has no hinge. Adult females are much larger than adult males.

SIMILAR SPECIES: The Eastern River Cooter, Red-eared Slider, and Painted Turtle lack the extremely long neck and "striped pants" on the hind legs.

FOOD: Young are carnivorous and become more herbivorous with age.

HABITAT: Still water preferably with abundant vegetation and ample basking sites.

REMARKS: The Chicken Turtle got its common name from its tasty meat. It is frequently encountered on land, especially in spring. It is highly diurnal and an avid basker. When captured, some are shy and remain in their shells while others hiss and scratch. The male has long front claws that are waved in the female's face during courtship. This species has temperature dependent sex determination. The scientific name *Deirochelys* means that this is a long-necked turtle. This turtle is protected by state law and cannot be taken out of the wild.

Hatchling

SIZE: Males 3.5 - 6.25 inches; Females 7 - 10.75 inches.

APPEARANCE: It has green skin with a yellow reticulate pattern. Behind each eye there is a yellow spot or blotch, which may have one or more projections that point toward the tail. One or more of the yellow lines on the neck reach the eye area. There is a dark bar through the eye. The carapace is low and covered with thin yellow or orange markings. The carapace has a slight mid-dorsal keel, which is more pronounced in juveniles. The posterior marginal scales (see Fig 6a) are serrated. There is no hinge in the plastron. The plastron of adults is plain and pale yellow or cream colored. Males have longer, thicker tails than females. The adult females have bigger heads and larger bodies than adult males.

SIMILAR SPECIES: The Ouachita Map Turtle has a more prominent mid-dorsal keel and two yellow blotches on each side of the face below the eye. The Mississippi Map Turtle has a more prominent keel, a yellow crescent behind the eye, and usually does not have a dark bar through the iris of the eye.

FOOD: Snails, crayfish, small fish, and insects.

HABITAT: Usually found in rivers or large bodies of water, but may also be found in smaller streams. Seems to prefer water with a gravel bottom. In Oklahoma it is known only from Delaware and Mayes Counties.

REMARKS: The Northern Map Turtle may be observed during the day while basking. It is wary and will escape into water if disturbed. This species has temperature dependent sex determination. The common name map turtle comes from the resemblance of the markings on the carapace to a topographic map. The name *Graptemys* means inscribed turtle and *geographica* refers to the yellow, map-like pattern on the shell. This turtle is an Oklahoma Species of Special Concern. It is protected by state law and cannot be removed from the wild.

Ouachita Map Turtle
Graptemys ouachitensis ouachitensis

SIZE: Males 3.5 - 5.25 inches; Females 5 - 10.75 inches.
APPEARANCE: The carapace is olive to brown with yellow oval markings and dark areas. The posterior end is serrated and a distinct keel extends down the midline of the carapace. A yellow oval or L-shaped blotch is found behind each eye and one or more yellow lines from the neck reach the eye. In addition, each side of the face usually has 2 more yellow blotches. One sits under the eye and the other sits on the lower jaw. The plastron is pale and lacks markings in adults. The plastron is not hinged. Adult females are much larger than males. Adult males have long claws on the front feet.

SIMILAR SPECIES: The Mississippi Map Turtle has yellow neck lines that do not reach the eye and does not have a dark blotch through the iris of the eye. The Northern Map Turtle has only one yellow blotch behind each eye and no blotches below the eye.

FOOD: A wide variety of invertebrates and plants.

HABITAT: Slow-moving stretches of rivers as well as lakes and ponds with ample basking spots.

REMARKS: The Ouachita Map Turtle may be seen sitting at the edge of water or as it swims near the surface of the water. It is diurnal and an avid basker. The male Ouachita Map Turtle uses its long claws to entice the female during courtship. During courtship, the male orients himself so that he is facing the female, stretches his forelegs forward and taps his claws on the female's head. The female lays 2 or 3 clutches of 6-13 eggs per year in Oklahoma. This species has temperature dependent sex determination. The common name map turtle comes from the resemblance of the markings on the carapace to a topographic map. The name *Graptemys* means inscribed turtle and *ouachitensis* is a reference to the Ouachita Mountains.

Mississippi Map Turtle
Graptemys pseudogeographica kohnii

Hatchling

SIZE: Males 3.5 - 5 inches; Females 6 - 10.75 inches.

APPEARANCE: The carapace is olive to brown and serrated along the posterior edge. A distinct keel with two black projections extends down the midline of the carapace. Each scute on the carapace has yellow circular patterns. The plastron is not hinged and shows dark lines on the seams between the scutes. A broad crescent-shaped yellow line behind the eye separates the eye from the yellow lines on the neck. This turtle has a white eye color and usually does not have a dark bar through the iris of the eye as seen in other aquatic turtles in Oklahoma. Adult females have larger bodies and heads than adult males. Males have long claws on the front feet.

SIMILAR SPECIES: The Ouachita Map Turtle has one or more yellow lines on each side of the neck that reach the eye area. The Northern Map Turtle has only one yellow spot or blotch behind each eye and also has one or more yellow lines on each side of the neck that reach the eye area.

FOOD: Primarily snails and small freshwater mussels, but also insects and aquatic plants.

HABITAT: Lakes, sloughs, and rivers with soft bottoms and aquatic plants.

REMARKS: This diurnal turtle is frequently found basking, but is wary and easily disturbed. A male uses its long front claws to stimulate the female during courtship. During courtship, the male orients himself so that he is facing the female, stretches his forelegs forward and taps his claws on the female's head. In parts of this turtle's range, water pollution, channelization, and habitat destruction have severely reduced the population size. This species has temperature dependent sex determination. The common name map turtle comes from the resemblance of the markings on the carapace to a topographic map. The name *Graptemys* means inscribed turtle and *pseudogeographica* means false map.

TURTLES

Eastern River Cooter
Pseudemys concinna concinna

Juvenile (left) and hatchling (right)

Adult

SIZE: 9-13 inches.

APPEARANCE: The broad and slightly flattened carapace is olive green or brownish with yellow markings. The plastron is usually a solid pale yellow, but the front half may have dark markings along the edges of the scutes that form an "X", which usually fades in adults. The plastron is not hinged. The skin is dark with yellow stripes. Most individuals have a rearward facing "C" on the second costal scute (see Fig. 6a). The chin looks flat when viewed from the front. The full-grown female is larger than the full-grown male. A male has long front claws. An old turtle may become dark and lose its color pattern.

SIMILAR SPECIES: The Red-eared Slider has a red blotch on the side of the head, a dark spot in the center of each plastral scute, and a rounded chin. The Western Chicken Turtle has a broad yellow stripe running down the front of the forelegs. These similar species lack the "C" found on the second costal scute of most Eastern River Cooters and are usually smaller.

FOOD: Young are primarily carnivorous, adults mostly herbivorous.

HABITAT: Rivers, lakes, and slow moving water with soft bottoms, basking sites, and adequate plant life.

REMARKS: This diurnal turtle is often seen basking. Many Eastern River Cooters may bask on a log. This turtle may be found away from water when it is crossing roads or traveling between ponds. The male uses its long front claws to excite the female during courtship. The male swims so that it is just above the female and then taps its claws on the female's head or moves them in front of the female's face. The name *concinna* means beautiful.

Three-toed Box Turtle
Terrapene carolina triunguis

Photos showing color and pattern variation

SIZE: 4.5-6 inches.

APPEARANCE: The carapace is relatively high and dome-shaped with a low keel running down the midline. The carapace is brown, but may have an indistinct pattern of yellow to orange lines and spots. An older individual may be patternless and have a pitted shell. The unpatterned plastron (see Fig. 6b) is tan to dark brown and has a hinge. In a male, the posterior part of the plastron is slightly concave. Some males have a great deal of red or orange coloration on the head. Normally, this turtle has only three toes on the hind foot, but occasionally it has four toes. The hind feet are rather stumpy and not webbed. The male usually has red eyes, whereas a female has yellow or brown eyes.

SIMILAR SPECIES: The Ornate Box Turtle lacks a keel on the carapace and has a distinct pattern on the plastron. The number of toes on the hind foot should not be used as the sole character to distinguish Three-toed Box Turtles from Ornate Box Turtles. The best character is the presence or absence of a pattern on the plastron (see photo in next account).

FOOD: Snails, earthworms, insects, carrion, plants, fungi, and fruits. Young are carnivorous and adults are mainly herbivorous.

HABITAT: Wooded areas and thickets.

REMARKS: The hinge on the plastron allows the box turtle to hide its head and legs inside its closed shell. If disturbed, this turtle frequently pulls its head and legs into its shell and remains there until it feels safe. This species has temperature dependent sex determination. It is diurnal, but does not bask a great deal like the aquatic members of this group of turtles. This is a terrestrial turtle, but it can swim and frequently crosses creeks. One individual was observed swimming across a ½-mile wide cove of Kerr Reservoir. *Terrapene* comes from a Native American word for turtle and *triunguis* means three-toed.

Ornate Box Turtle
Terrapene ornata ornata

Female

Male

Hatchling with egg-tooth still attached

SIZE: 4-5 inches.

APPEARANCE: It has a high-domed carapace (see Fig. 6a) that normally lacks a keel along the midline. Each brown scute has bright yellow lines. Frequently, a yellow line extends down the midline of the carapace. The plastron has a hinge (see Fig. 6b) and is distinctly patterned with yellow and black markings. The male has a concave plastron. There are four (sometimes three) toes on the hind foot. The hind feet are stumpy and not webbed. The eyes of a male are red and the eyes of a female are yellow or brown.

SIMILAR SPECIES: The Three-toed Box Turtle has a keel on top of the carapace, a patternless plastron, and normally lives in wooded areas. The number of toes on the hind foot should not be the only characteristic used to separate the two species of box turtles. The presence or absence of a pattern on the plastron is the best character to distinguish between the box turtles in Oklahoma (see photo below).

FOOD: Mostly insects but also plant material and carrion.

HABITAT: Found statewide in open prairies with sandy soil. It is most abundant in short-grass prairies. Occasionally found in wooded habitat.

REMARKS: This turtle can close its shell very tightly when threatened or in danger. It can pull its head and four legs completely inside the shell. The Ornate Box Turtle has temperature dependent sex determination. This is a terrestrial turtle, but it is a good swimmer. Like the Three-toed Box Turtle, it rarely basks. It is diurnal, although one individual was observed crossing a road on a warm summer night. This species was once collected in large numbers for the pet trade. It is now illegal, in Oklahoma, to sell box turtles that have been taken from the wild. *Terrapene* comes from a Native American word for turtle and *ornata* refers to the ornate pattern on the shell.

Plastron comparison of Three-toed Box Turtle (left) and Ornate Box Turtle (right)

Adult

Older (melanistic) male

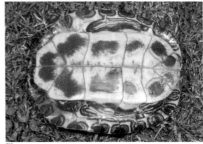

Plastron

SIZE: 5-8 inches.

APPEARANCE: The carapace has rough scutes and varies from green with yellow reticulation to plain and dark. The head and legs are green with yellow lines. Usually there is a broad, red stripe on each side of the head behind the eye. The hingeless plastron is yellow with one large dark blotch near the center of each scute. Some older males may have a uniformly dark carapace with no pattern. These individuals are called melanistic males. The large red stripe on each side of the head may be obscure in adults. The chin of this turtle looks round when viewed from the front. A full-grown adult female is larger than a full-grown male. An adult male has long claws on the front feet.

SIMILAR SPECIES: No other pond turtle has one dark blotch per scute on the plastron. The Eastern River Cooter lacks a red spot on the head, has an inverted "C" on the second costal scute, and the back half of the plastron is plain, pale yellow without dark blotches. The Western Painted Turtle has red on the carapace and the Southern Painted Turtle has a plain plastron. The Western Chicken Turtle has "striped pants", has a very long neck, and lacks a red spot on each side of the head.

FOOD: Juveniles are carnivorous, eating insects, snails, crayfish, fish, and tadpoles. Adults are omnivorous and mainly eat plant material.

HABITAT: Slow rivers, streams, ponds, lakes, and swamps with soft bottoms and ample vegetation.

REMARKS: The Red-eared Slider is the most abundant turtle in Oklahoma and may reach high densities. This turtle is an avid basker and can be seen on logs or near shore during the day. Often many are seen basking communally on a log. Although it is most commonly seen in association with water, this turtle will occasionally travel long distances over land from one water source to another. Adult males may move several miles over land. Nests also may be found as far as a mile from water. The long front claws of the male are used in courtship to entice the female. The male orients himself so that he is facing the female and then stretches his forelegs forward and taps his claws on the female's head. This species has temperature dependent sex determination. The typical size range is given above, but there is a record of an 11-inch long individual. This species may bask on sunny winter days and has been observed moving around under an ice covering in a pond. The species name *scripta* is in reference to the fact that the scutes look like they have been written upon and *elegans* means elegant.

Hatchling

Midland Smooth Softshell
Apalone mutica mutica

Nostrils lacking projections

SIZE: 4.5-14 inches.

APPEARANCE: This turtle has a flat, leathery shell that lacks scutes, is olive to orangish-brown, and has dark markings. An older male may lose its color pattern. The edges of the shell are soft and flexible. The plastron is white to gray. The anterior edge of the carapace lacks spines and there are no projections in the nostrils (see above diagram). The neck and nose are long. There is reduced or no pattern on the front legs. Each foot has three claws. A female has longer claws on the back feet and a male has longer claws on the front feet. A full-grown adult female is larger than a full-grown adult male. The male has a thicker, longer tail than a female.

SIMILAR SPECIES: The Spiny Softshell Turtle has a projection in each nostril, spines along the front edge of the carapace, and patterned front legs.

FOOD: Fish, insects, amphibians, mollusks, worms, and infrequently fruit and plants.

HABITAT: Streams, rivers, and occasionally impoundments, preferably with sandy or soft bottoms and moderate to fast water flow.

REMARKS: This species is usually aquatic but will bask on sandbars or lake shores. In rivers it is found most often in shallow water near sandbars. Full-grown females can be found in deeper water than the males. Juveniles prefer small, warm pools by the river's edge. During the day this turtle usually buries itself in the sand or soft mud in shallow water of the river bed. Sometimes the eyes and nostrils stick out above the sand, but the rest of the turtle remains buried. When it needs to breathe, it extends its neck up through the water column only exposing the nostrils above the water surface. This turtle is a strong, fast swimmer, but can run amazingly fast. It normally has a milder temperament than a Spiny Softshell Turtle. Softshells are the only native Oklahoma turtles with genetic sex determination instead of temperature dependent sex determination. *Apalone* means soft swimmer.

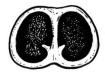

Nostrils showing projections

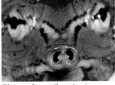

Photo of nostril projections

TURTLES

SIZE: 7-18 inches.

APPEARANCE: This turtle's flat, leathery shell lacks scutes and is soft and flexible. The carapace of the male is rougher (like sandpaper) than that of the female. Both the nose and the neck are long. All four legs usually have dark mottling. The plastron is white to yellow and lacks markings. Spines extend from the anterior end of the carapace. Inside each nostril there is a small projection or ridge (see above diagram and small photo). There are three claws on each foot. Both sexes have a dark line along the edge of the carapace. A full-grown adult female is larger than a full-grown male. The male has a thicker, longer tail than the female. The Western Spiny Softshell has a carapace that is olive to tan with dark circular patterns. The Pallid Spiny Softshell has white spots or raised projections mostly on the posterior half of the carapace and no dark circular patterns.

SIMILAR SPECIES: The Smooth Softshell Turtle lacks spines on the anterior edge of the carapace, has no projection in the nostrils, and no or reduced pattern on the front legs.

FOOD: Crayfish, insects, mollusks, earthworms, fish, amphibians, and carrion.

HABITAT: Statewide in rivers, streams, lakes and ponds with sandy or soft bottoms.

REMARKS: It can be seen basking near water but usually stays in the water buried in the sand with only the nostrils exposed to air. It is a very fast swimmer and can run quickly over short distances. This species has a nasty temperament if disturbed. Softshells are the only native Oklahoma turtles with genetic sex determination instead of temperature dependent sex determination. *Apalone* means soft swimmer, *spinifera* refers to the spines on the shell, and *pallida* means pale.

SUBSPECIES: Western Spiny Softshell (*Apalone spinifera hartwegi*), in the northern ⅔ of Oklahoma; Pallid Spiny Softshell (*Apalone spinifera pallida*), in southern ⅓ of Oklahoma in the Red River Drainage.

113

Lizards (Order Squamata)

BEHAVIOR

Lizards control their body temperatures primarily by behavioral means such as basking or sitting on or next to a warm object. Some help regulate their body temperature also by changing the color or reflective properties of their skin. In captivity they need to have warmer temperatures during the day than at night. Many lizards will not eat or digest their food properly at low body temperatures. Like all reptiles, they are most active during the warm months of the year. During the winter they are inactive and stay in burrows in protected areas. All of Oklahoma's native lizards are active during the day. Only the introduced gecko species is active at night.

Oklahoma lizards exhibit varied life-styles. Glass lizards are burrowers. Iguanids and whiptails are basking lizards and are relatively easy to find on warm mornings. Skinks live under leaf litter or debris. Lizards are mainly ground dwellers, but all can swim and some may occasionally escape danger by running into a pond or stream. Many lizards are adept climbers and some, such as the Prairie Lizard, may scamper into trees whereas the anole is usually found in trees, shrubs, or vines.

ANATOMY

Lizards have good senses of hearing and sight and are able to monitor their environment quite well. Males and females differ in appearance in some species of lizards, a phenomenon called sexual dimorphism. In general, males are more brightly colored than females, and males of some species have blue or red coloration on their throats, sides of the head, and/or body, especially during the breeding season. In some species the newborns have different color patterns than adults. For example, young skinks have bright blue tails and adults do not.

At first it may be difficult to distinguish some lizards from salamanders. Both groups of animals have long bodies, long tails, and four legs. However, lizards have scales, claws on their toes and external ear openings, except for the earless lizards. In contrast, salamanders, which are amphibians, have smooth, moist skin and lack scales, claws, and ear openings.

Reptilian kidneys produce a waste substance called uric acid, which is excreted as a thick white paste. Some lizard species also have salt glands that excrete salt waste through the nostrils, and in those species, you can often see salt residue on the nose. The kidneys and salt glands act to conserve water. All Oklahoma lizards are strictly carnivorous and most are chiefly insectivorous. Lizards shed their outer skin layer periodically, as do snakes. In contrast to snakes, lizards normally shed their skin in pieces and often ingest part or all of the skin. Unlike snakes, during the shedding process a lizard's vision is not impaired because the lizard does not shed its eye covering.

REPRODUCTION

All Oklahoma lizards lay eggs. Skinks and glass lizards guard their eggs, but most Oklahoma lizards abandon their eggs once they are laid. In some of our species, males and sometimes females exhibit bright body colors during the breeding season. This color change is brought on by changes in hormone levels.

CONSERVATION

There are no venomous lizards in Oklahoma. Some of the largest lizards may be able to bite hard enough to break the skin, but as a group they are harmless to humans and consume many insect pests.

Snakes and birds are the main predators of lizards, but habitat loss due to agricultural development and other human activities takes a greater toll on lizard populations. Feral and domestic cats that are allowed to live outside also kill numerous lizards. Pesticides that kill insects eaten by lizards have a negative effect on lizard populations by directly affecting lizards or by decreasing their food sources. Overcollection of lizards for the pet trade may also greatly impact lizard populations.

GROUPS OF LIZARDS

There are five groups of lizards in Oklahoma. Of these, the iguanid lizards are the most diverse and commonly encountered. They include the anole, collared lizard, side-blotched lizard, horned lizard, earless lizards, and prairie lizards.

The iguanid lizards are alert and some species are territorial. Some change color in response to temperature, hormones, and "emotional" stimuli. Many are brightest in color during the breeding season. Iguanids typically exhibit displays of head-bobs, pushups, mouth gapes, throat distention, and body inflation. Displays are used in communication such as territorial disputes and courtship.

Their boldness during the breeding season and their visibility while basking make the iguanids among our easiest reptiles to observe. If approached slowly and quietly, they will often allow close observation for considerable lengths of time. These lizards bask to elevate their body temperatures. Most iguanids prefer daytime body temperatures of 95 to 100° F and in captivity they will not eat if they cannot warm up during the day.

The whiptails and racerunners in Oklahoma belong to the genus *Cnemidophorus*. These lizards make quick, nervous movements as they forage. They are normally active during the warmest portions of the day. The scales on the back are very small and granular looking. The belly has eight rows of large, rectangular scales and the upper surface of the tail has scales larger than those on the back. The back is smooth and the tail is slightly rough.

Some species in this group are unisexual, meaning only females exist. Reproduction occurs through the development of unfertilized eggs, which hatch into female lizards identical to their mothers. *Cnemidophorus tesselatus* is Oklahoma's only unisexual lizard. All individuals in the population are female and the young are clones of the mother.

Skinks have scales that feel like smooth vinyl. Skinks can break off their tails easily when captured (tail autotomy). The tail then flails about and holds the predator's attention while the skink scurries off. This occurs with virtually no blood loss, and the skink eventually regenerates its tail. This "new tail" is different in structure and appearance from the original tail. The name blue-tailed skink is often used, but there is no species with this name in Oklahoma. Five of the six Oklahoma skink species have blue tails as hatchlings.

Labial scales on the upper lip and presence or absence of a small postnasal scale (see Figs. 9 and 10) are used to distinguish among several species of skinks. Postmental scales are used to distinguish the coal skink from some other skinks (see Figs. 11a and 11b). Viewing skinks up-close is the most accurate way to ensure correct identification.

Glass lizards are legless. Each scale is supported from the underside by a bony plate. A fold, the dorsolateral groove, extends down the side of the body. These lizards are terrestrial and able to autotomize their tails like skinks. Although common, they are rarely seen because they spend most of their time in burrows.

One gecko species occurs in the state, and it is not native but introduced from the Mediterranean area. This is the only nocturnal lizard species found in Oklahoma. Geckos are very prone to tail autotomy when distressed.

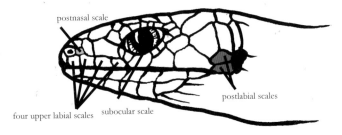

FIG. 9. - Head of Five-lined Skink showing four upper labial scales, subocular scale, postnasal scale and postlabial scales

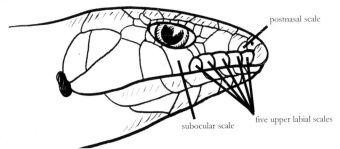

FIG. 10. - Head of Broad-headed skink showing five upper labial scales, subocular scale and postnasal scale

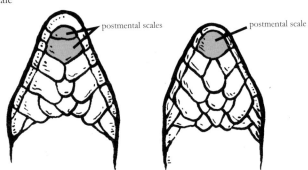

FIG. 11A. - Ventral view of a Southern Prairie Skink head showing two postmental scales

FIG. 11B. - Ventral view of a Coal Skink head showing a single postmental scale

Male displaying dewlap

SIZE: 5-8 inches.

APPEARANCE: Its dorsal color can change from green to brown or to a mottled green-brown depending on temperature or "emotional" state (fighting males are usually a mottled green). This lizard has a pointed face. The male has a pink dewlap that sits below the jaw and can be extended out. The pink color is visible only during display. The dewlap of the female is much smaller and white or pale pink. The male is a bit larger than the female. The bottoms of the toes have ridges, which contain microscopic hairs with spatulate ends that allow the lizard to climb up many surfaces, including glass.

SIMILAR SPECIES: No other native Oklahoma lizard has wide toes with ridges on the underside and a long tapered face.

FOOD: Insects and spiders.

HABITAT: Found around human dwellings, trees, posts, or shrubs. Highly arboreal, it may scamper high into trees. Often it is found in trees and shrubs near water. It even spends the night in trees and shrubs.

REMARKS: Because a Northern Green Anole can change colors more rapidly than our other lizards, it is often incorrectly called a chameleon. The true chameleon is not native to the United States and is much more adept at color change than our Northern Green Anole. The male is territorial and will display by extending its dewlap, doing pushups, and bobbing its head if another male intrudes into the resident's territory. Unlike most Oklahoma lizards that lay one or two clutches of eggs per year, the Northern Green Anole lays multiple, very small clutches of eggs through the summer.

LIZARDS

117

Female (left) and male (right)

Color variation from southwestern Oklahoma

Hatchling

SIZE: 8-14 inches.

APPEARANCE: It has two black rings that form a partial collar around the neck. This species shows sexual dimorphism. The male is blue-green to olive-green with many light spots and a golden or yellow throat. Blue-green males are found in the Wichita Mountains and Glass Mountains. The more common color for males is green. The male has a larger head and larger femoral pores on the underside of the thigh than the female. The female is tan with many light spots and a white throat. The female develops red bars on the body at the beginning of the breeding season. These disappear after the breeding season. The juvenile is tan to yellow with dark bars alternating with yellow to orange bars.

SIMILAR SPECIES: None in Oklahoma.

FOOD: Insects, especially grasshoppers, spiders, other lizards, small snakes, and possibly newborn rodents.

HABITAT: Found statewide except in the coastal plain region in extreme southeastern Oklahoma; Rocky outcrops and riprap on dams of impoundments.

REMARKS: This diurnal, territorial lizard is the Oklahoma State Reptile. It is feisty and will bite. One adult male bit right through its captor's fingernail. Although known as the "Mountain Boomer," it has no voice but will hiss when threatened. When running, this lizard may run on its back legs with its front legs off the ground. Males are territorial with 1-9 females defended in each territory. The seasonal color change associated with breeding is caused by hormone changes. Temperature and the presence of other males in the area also influence a male's color. Adult males become scarce in August and adult females become scarce in September. Hatchlings start to appear in late July and may grow up to 1mm per day during their first season. Young of the year may remain active until October. *Crotaphytus* refers to the relatively large head and *collaris* to the collar around the neck.

LIZARDS

Adult male

Male Great Plains Earless Lizard

Female Prairie Earless Lizard in breeding color

LIZARDS

120

SIZE: 4-5 inches.

APPEARANCE: This lizard has two folds of skin across the throat and, as the name implies, no external ear openings. Its dorsal color varies from gray to gray-brown. The dorsal surface has 9-14 dark brown blotches. No spots occur on the underside of the tail. The male has a grayer throat than the female. The male has a pair of black bars behind the foreleg surrounded by blue borders. These blue areas can be displayed during courtship behavior. The female may have reduced or absent black bars that are not surrounded by blue. The female has an orange throat and sides during the breeding season. A juvenile resembles the adult female. The Great Plains Earless Lizard has two rows of blotches on each side of the back. The male has small white dots on the back. The Prairie Earless Lizard usually has a single row of long bars (fused blotches) on each side of the back. Occasionally, it has two rows of blotches. The white dots are reduced in males of this subspecies compared to those of the Great Plains Earless Lizard.

SIMILAR SPECIES: Other lizards have external ear openings on the sides of the head.

FOOD: Insects and spiders.

HABITAT: It prefers open sandy areas with sparse vegetation. This species is associated with the shortgrass to mixed prairie.

REMARKS: This is a diurnal, territorial species. The territory holder will do head-bobs and push-ups to chase others from intruding into its territory. If pursued by a predator it will run a short distance then burrow down into the sandy soil to escape. Although the word "earless," is in this lizard's name, it can hear. The Great Plains Earless Lizard used to be called the Northern Earless Lizard and the Prairie Earless Lizard used to be called the Eastern Earless Lizard. The name *maculata* means spotted. The species is an Oklahoma Species of Special Concern. Both earless lizards are protected by state law and cannot be removed from the wild.

SUBSPECIES: Great Plains Earless Lizard (*Holbrookia maculata maculata*), in the western ¼ of Oklahoma, including the panhandle; Prairie Earless Lizard (*Holbrookia maculata perspicua*), in the west central ¼ of Oklahoma.

Male Prairie Earless Lizard

Photos showing color variation

Tiny Hatchling

SIZE: 2.25-4 inches.

APPEARANCE: This lizard has a flat body. The two central horns on the back of the head are longer than the two lateral horns. There are two rows of fringe scales (small, spiny scales along each lateral side of the body). The background color varies with the soil color, but is usually tan, reddish, yellow, gray, or brown with a light colored stripe down the midline. The ear openings are readily visible.

SIMILAR SPECIES: No other Oklahoma lizard has a flat body shape or horns on the back of the head.

FOOD: Primarily ants and small beetles, but will eat other small insects and spiders.

HABITAT: Dry, sandy areas with sparse to moderately vegetated grassland with bare ground, forbs, and shrubs.

REMARKS: The Texas Horned Lizard is a diurnal species active at temperatures above 75° F. It displays the remarkable behavior of squirting blood from its eyes in response to threats from dog-like predators. It is commonly called "horned toad" or "horny toad". This species does poorly in captivity. It needs a ready supply of ants to survive, but not all ant species are eaten by the Texas Horned Lizard. Populations of the Texas Horned Lizard are historically known from the western 3/4 of Oklahoma, but are apparently in decline throughout the entire range of this species. Insecticide use, imported fire ants, habitat alteration, highway mortality, and commercial exploitation have all been suggested as possible causes for population declines. Tiny quarter-sized hatchlings appear in late summer. The clutch size of this animal in Oklahoma is around 13-20 eggs. The name *Phrynosoma* means "toad body" and *cornutum* means horned. The species is an Oklahoma Species of Special Concern. It is protected by state law and cannot be removed from the wild.

Another color variant

LIZARDS

Ecomorph found in western 2/3 of Oklahoma except the counties along the Red River

Ecomorph found in Cimarron County

Ecomorph found in eastern 1/3 of Oklahoma

Belly of male showing breeding season colors

Ecomorph found along Red River in the western 2/3 of Oklahoma

SIZE: 4-7.25 inches.

APPEARANCE: The Prairie Lizard in Oklahoma is highly variable. There are four color varieties, called ecomorphs, found in Oklahoma whose appearances are determined by the local habitat color. Its dorsal body color varies from gray to brown. It may have two light, longitudinal stripes on the back, and its scales are keeled. The male has blue patches on the throat and belly, especially during the breeding season, which can be displayed during courtship behavior. The females have wavy lines extending from side-to-side along their backs and much less blue on their bellies. Juveniles look like adults. The ecomorph found in the eastern 1/3 of Oklahoma lacks light, longitudinal stripes on the back, and the male has black on the throat and belly. The ecomorph in Cimarron County has a yellowish-orange cast to the throat and lips. This is more obvious in the male, especially during breeding season. The ecomorph found in the western 2/3 of Oklahoma, except along the Red River, has small dark markings on the back, dorsal to the light, longitudinal stripes (in the other ecomorphs these dark markings are larger). There are two light, longitudinal stripes on each side of the body. The ecomorph found along the Red River in the western 2/3 of Oklahoma has less distinct longitudinal stripes than the other ecomorphs.

SIMILAR SPECIES: A Lesser Earless Lizard lacks ear openings and an Eastern Side-blotched Lizard has a dark dorsolateral blotch and complete fold of skin on the throat.

FOOD: Small insects and spiders.

HABITAT: This species is found statewide. Its habitat varies from sunny woodlands to sandy regions with rocky outcrops. It is often found climbing trees, stumps, and rock outcrops.

REMARKS: The male is territorial and may perform several displays including push-ups and head bobs when an intruder enters its territory. Until recently the Prairie Lizard in Oklahoma was split into four subspecies. The subspecies are no longer recognized, but the four distinct color varieties are each referred to as an ecomorph of the Prairie Lizard.

Ecomorph found in Cimarron County: male above and female below

Color variations

SIZE: 4-5 inches.

APPEARANCE: This small, brownish lizard has a single black spot on each side behind the front leg and a single complete fold of skin across the throat. There are numerous dark dorsal blotches and normally a pale thin stripe from the eye to tail, which is more prominent in the female. The male has a light blue tint to the skin of the throat and sides of the body, and blue, dorsal flecks. The scales in the middle of the back are larger and rougher than those along the sides.

SIMILAR SPECIES: A Prairie Lizard lacks dorsolateral spots and a complete fold of skin on the throat. A Lesser Earless Lizard has no ear openings, two dark spots behind the arm, and two folds of skin on the throat.

FOOD: Insects, ticks, mites, and spiders.

HABITAT: Foothills, open sandy or rocky areas with short grasses.

REMARKS: The Eastern Side-blotched Lizard is a diurnal ground dweller, but it also climbs on rocks and boulders. It may be observed while basking. Although this species is common throughout much of its range, it barely gets into the southwestern corner of the state and is rarely encountered in Oklahoma. It has been recorded only in Harmon and Jackson Counties. This species will autotomize its tail if a predator grasps it. This lizard is protected by state law and cannot be taken out of the wild.

SIZE: 6.5-11 inches.

APPEARANCE: From the neck to the hips, it has seven or eight light yellow to white dorsal stripes. There are three sets of light stripes on each side, and the mid-dorsal stripe may be single or double. There is a single row of pale spots in the dark ground color on each of the lizard's sides. The dark dorsolateral ground color (wide dark stripe) does not extend onto the tail behind the rear legs. There is a patch of enlarged scales on the rear of each forearm. The male has a pinkish throat and dark blue chest and belly, which can be displayed during courtship. The female has a white to pink throat and white belly. The juvenile has a rusty colored tail and may lack spots on the side. A hatchling has a pink to red tail and hips.

SIMILAR SPECIES: The Prairie Racerunner lacks spots within the dark ground color on the sides and lacks the patch of enlarged scales on the rear of each forearm. The Prairie Racerunner is normally bright green at the front end of the body.

FOOD: Spiders and insects, especially grasshoppers, termites, and caterpillars.

HABITAT: Prairie grasslands or arid, rocky areas near water.

REMARKS: The Texas Spotted Whiptail is diurnal and less wary than the closely related Prairie Racerunner. It may stop to see what is chasing it when pursued. It is active on warm days. It moves in an almost constant, jerky way when foraging. The term *gularis* refers to the throat. Some scientists believe this lizard should be in the genus *Aspidoselis* making the scientific name *Aspidoscelis gularis gularis* (See p.4).

127

Prairie Racerunner

Eastern Six-lined Racerunner

Head close-up of Eastern Six-lined Racerunner

LIZARDS

128

SIZE: 6-10.5 inches.

APPEARANCE: This quick moving lizard is long and slender. It has six or seven light stripes extending from the head onto the tail. The dorsal scales are granular and are non-overlapping. During the breeding season the male's belly has a bluish cast. The base of the male's tail is larger, it has a broader head, and the femoral pores on the underside of the thigh are more obvious than in the female. A newborn has a blue tail. The Prairie Racerunner has seven (or rarely eight) light stripes down the back. There are three on each side and one on the mid-dorsal line (which occasionally is divided). The dark dorsolateral ground color (wide, dark stripes) extends onto the tail behind the rear legs. The ground color of the front part of the body is usually bright lime green and less often brownish. The Eastern Six-lined Racerunner is similar to the Prairie Racerunner but has a dark ground color with six pale longitudinal stripes.

SIMILAR SPECIES: The Texas Spotted Whiptail has a row of light spots in its dark ground color down each side of the body and a patch of enlarged scales on the rear of each forearm.

FOOD: Grasshoppers, crickets, moths, other insects, spiders, small scorpions, and snails. In captivity it will eat smaller lizards.

HABITAT: Dry, open, sunny areas. They especially prefer sandy areas.

REMARKS: This lizard spends much of its activity time moving about. The Prairie Racerunner prefers high body temperatures and is diurnal. During inactivity it hides under rocks, goes into another animal's burrow, or digs its own. The adult male will expose the blue belly during display behavior. The term *sexlineatus* means six lines and *viridis* means green. Some scientists believe this lizard should be in the genus *Aspidoscelis* making the scientific names *Aspidoscelis sexlineata sexlineata* and *Aspidoscelis sexlineata viridis* (See p. 4).

SUBSPECIES: Prairie Racerunner (*Cnemidophorus sexlineatus viridis*) - statewide except in the coastal plain region of extreme southeastern Oklahoma. Eastern Six-lined Racerunner (*Cnemidophorus sexlineatus sexlineatus*) - the coastal plain region of extreme southeastern Oklahoma.

Hatchling Prairie Racerunner: note blue tail

SIZE: 11-15.5 inches.

APPEARANCE: The ground color of this lizard is yellow to off-white. Six pale lines are sometimes visible on the back. There are dark blotches in rows down the back, giving the lizard an overall checkered appearance. The chin and belly are pale. There are enlarged scales across the back of the throat (anterior to the gular fold). The long tail is almost three times the body length.

SIMILAR SPECIES: Other *Cnemidophorus* lack a checkered or blotched pattern and tend to have either a greenish or dark ground color. The Checkered Whiptail is larger than the other *Cnemidophorus* found in Oklahoma.

FOOD: Spiders, scorpions, and insects.

HABITAT: Sand or gravel areas with rocks and some vegetation.

REMARKS: This is mainly a unisexual species. It arose as a hybrid from matings between other *Cnemidophorus* species. Unmated females lay eggs that produce young females that are identical to their mother. This process is called parthenogenesis. Some males have been found, but most populations consist of only females. These lizards are often found in isolated small groups. The Checkered Whiptail is less wary than most whiptails and is easier to approach. The name *tesselatus* means checkered. This lizard is protected by state law and has a closed season, meaning it cannot be taken out of the wild. Some scientists believe this lizard should be in the genus *Aspidoscelis* making the scientific name *Aspidocelis tesselata* (See p. 4).

Chin showing single
postmental scale

SIZE: 5-7 inches

APPEARANCE: The adult is brown to olive brown in color. A broad dark dorsolateral stripe on each side of the body includes 2 ½ to 4 scale rows and is bordered above and below by a thin, lightly colored stripe. The dark dorsolateral stripe is wider than that found in other Oklahoma *Eumeces*. The upper light stripe is located on the 3rd and 4th scale row from the mid-dorsal line. The head lacks light colored lines. There is only one postmental scale (see Fig. 11b) and there is no postnasal scale (see Figs. 9 and 10). The scales are shiny and smooth. The male has red-orange jaws during the breeding season. The juvenile is plain black with a blue tail.

SIMILAR SPECIES: The other species of *Eumeces* in Oklahoma that lacks a postnasal scale is the Prairie Skink, and it has two postmental scales, but the Southern Coal Skink has only one. The Prairie Skink, juvenile Five-lined Skink, and Broad-headed Skink have a broad dark stripe on each side, but the stripe is less than 2½ scale-rows wide. The Little Brown Skink is more salamander-like in shape and has a long, thin body with no light colored line above and below the dark lateral stripe. A hatchling Great Plains Skink is also dark with a blue tail, but has white markings on top of the head and above the lips.

FOOD: Insects and spiders.

HABITAT: Humid, wooded hillsides with leaf litter or stones, often near water.

REMARKS: The Southern Coal Skink is a secretive, diurnal, terrestrial lizard most frequently observed in March and April. It spends much of its time in leaf litter but will escape pursuit by jumping into water. The female protects her eggs. If seized by the tail, it will autotomize it. The separated, wiggling tail distracts the predator while the skink runs to safety. *Eumeces* means good length, referring to tail length and *anthracinus* means coal, the color of the lateral stripe. Some scientists believe this lizard should be in the genus *Plestiodon* making the scientific name *Plestiodon anthracinus pluvialis*. See p. 4.

LIZARDS

Male (left), Juvenile (top right) and Female (lower right)

Male (left) and Juvenile (right)

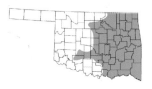

Gravid female

SIZE: 5-8 inches.

APPEARANCE: This lizard has five pale, broad stripes on a dark background. An older male sometimes loses the five pale stripes and becomes solid brown. A female normally retains the light lines. Usually there is a dark, lateral stripe on the third and fourth scales down from the mid-dorsal line. During the breeding season, the male develops a red-orange color on his jaw. The juvenile has five pale stripes on a black body and a brilliant blue tail. Hatchlings, juveniles, and females have two light lines on the head. Usually a Five-lined Skink has a postnasal scale, four upper labial scales anterior to the subocular scale, and two postlabial scales (see Fig. 9). It has shiny, smooth scales.

SIMILAR SPECIES: Color pattern is not always a reliable tool for distinguishing between a Five-lined Skink and other skinks since the Five-lined Skink shows great variety in color pattern. The Broad-headed Skink normally has five upper labial scales anterior to the sub-ocular scale and is lacking or has one small postlabial scale. An adult Broad-headed Skink gets considerably larger than an adult Five-lined Skink. The Southern Prairie Skink and the Southern Coal Skink lack a postnasal scale. The Southern Coal Skink has one postmental scale (see Fig. 11b) and never has light lines on the head.

FOOD: Adult and larval insects, spiders, earthworms, crustaceans, snails, baby mice, and small lizards.

HABITAT: Found in woodlands, near homes, and in moist areas with rock piles and logs.

REMARKS: This diurnal lizard may be seen basking on tree trunks and stumps. This skink is at home in gardens and backyards. Eggs are often laid in rotting piles of wood chips or saw dust or under rocks and logs. The female stays with and attends her eggs. The female moves her eggs within the nest to keep them moist. This lizard will autotomize its tail if the tail is grabbed by a predator. The tail then wiggles on the ground, attracting the predator's attention, while the rest of the skink runs to safety. *Eumeces* means good length and refers to the tail length. The name *fasciata* means that this is a striped lizard. Some scientists believe this lizard should be in the genus *Plestiodon* making the scientific name *Plestiodon fasciatus* (See p. 4).

Juvenile

Adult male

Adult male showing triangular jaw

SIZE: 6.5-12.75 inches.

APPEARANCE: The adult is large with a uniform brown color or five light stripes on the back. Stripes are usually absent in a large male, but retained in a female. During breeding season the male's jaws turn orange-red. When viewed from above, the head of the adult male may look triangular. A juvenile has obvious stripes, a black body, and a bright blue tail. The juvenile and the adult female have two light stripes on the head, which are sometimes broken. This species has shiny, smooth scales. It usually has a postnasal scale, five upper labial scales anterior to the subocular scale, and lacks or has one postlabial scale (see Fig. 10).

SIMILAR SPECIES: The Five-lined Skink usually has four upper labial scales and two postlabial scales. A Broad-headed Skink may have four upper labial scales anterior to the subocular scale on one side of the head and five on the other side of the head, making identification difficult. A young Broad-headed Skink is difficult to distinguish from a young Five-lined Skink. The Southern Prairie Skink and Southern Coal Skink have no postnasal scale. The Southern Coal Skink has one postmental scale.

FOOD: Insects, spiders, and smaller reptiles.

HABITAT: Frequently found in trees, it prefers moist, wooded areas and is sometimes observed under leaf litter or loose bark of dead trees.

REMARKS: This diurnal lizard is large and can bite, sometimes breaking human skin. The female attends her eggs and does not abandon them. It will autotomize its tail, if seized. The separated, wiggling tail distracts the predator while the skink runs to safety. This skink is more likely to find food by climbing into trees than Oklahoma's other skinks. *Eumeces* means good length, in reference to tail length and *laticeps* means broad head. Some scientists believe this lizard should be in the genus *Plestiodon* making the scientific name *Plestiodon laticeps* (See p. 4).

LIZARDS

Hatchling

SIZE: 6.5-13.75 inches.

APPEARANCE: The adult has a plain tan belly and dark edged, tan scales on the back. The scales' dark edges may look like lines on the back. On the side of the body, the scales do not lie in horizontal, parallel rows (as seen on other Oklahoma skinks), but run obliquely. A hatchling's tail is dark blue. Its body is glossy black with white dots on the head, along the lips, and on the hind legs. The scales are smooth and shiny. This is the state's largest skink.

SIMILAR SPECIES: No other Oklahoma skink has oblique, lateral scale rows. The hatchling may resemble a young Southern Coal Skink or a Southern Prairie Skink, but a hatchling Great Plains Skink has white spots on the top of the head and along the lips.

FOOD: Insects, spiders, snails, and small lizards.

HABITAT: Rocky, open grasslands.

REMARKS: This is the largest native skink found in the United States. Because of its large size, this lizard can bite hard if it is handled. It may then twirl and twist while pinching the handler's skin. This diurnal species can be quite numerous in its preferred habitat. Normally it is found under flat rocks on grassland hillsides. It burrows in the soil or uses the burrows of small rodents. This lizard almost never basks, but heats itself by sitting under warm rocks. The female attends her eggs rather than abandoning them. If seized by the tail, this lizard will autotomize its tail. The tail then moves around, attracting the predator's attention, while the rest of the skink escapes. *Eumeces* means good length in reference to the tail length. The term *obsoletus* is a reference to the lack of lines on the back of this skink. Some scientists believe this lizard should be in the genus *Plestiodon* making the scientific name *Plestiodon obsoletus* (See p. 4).

135

SIZE: 5-7.25 inches.

APPEARANCE: The body is tan to brown or gray with a dark, lateral stripe no more than two scale rows wide extending onto the tail. This wide dark stripe is bordered above and below by a thin, light stripe. The upper light stripe on each side is on the 4th and some-times 5th scale row from the mid-dorsal line. Normally there is a thin dark stripe above the upper light stripe on each side. Rarely there may be a faded mid-dorsal stripe, but usually the mid-dorsal area lacks any pattern. There are two postmental scales and no postnasal scales (see Figs. 9 and 11a). A breeding male has an orange-red chin. A juvenile has a blue tail. The scales are shiny and smooth.

SIMILAR SPECIES: A Southern Coal Skink has a dorsolateral dark stripe that extends onto the tail, but it is over two scale rows wide. The Southern Coal Skink also lacks a post-nasal scale, but has only one postmental scale. An older male Five-lined Skink may look like a Southern Prairie Skink, but it has a postnasal scale. The Broad-headed Skink has a postna-sal scale.

FOOD: Insects, spiders, and snails.

HABITAT: It is found under boards, leaf litter, or rocky, open grassland, usually near water.

REMARKS: This lizard may be diurnal or active near dusk and dawn. It is secretive and hides when disturbed, but is found in more open areas than other skinks. It is more likely to be active in spring than in the summer heat. The female stays with her eggs. This species will autotomize its tail if grabbed by the tail by a predator. When this happens the tail wiggles about, attracts the predator's attention, and the skink runs to safety. *Eumeces* means good length in reference to the tail length and *septentrionalis* means northern. Some scientists believe this lizard should be in the genus *Plestiodon* making the scientific name *Plestiodon septentrionalis obtusirostris*. In addition, some scientists consider this lizard to be a distinct species (See p. 4).

SIZE: 3-5 inches.

APPEARANCE: This small skink has a golden to dark brown back with a dark dorsolateral stripe extending from the nostril onto the tail. In some individuals the stripe is barely noticeable. The dark stripe does not have a light stripe running next to it. The belly is gray, yellow, or white. This skink has smooth, shiny scales and may have black dots on the back. The tail is longer than the length of the head and body. Young lack bright blue tails.

SIMILAR SPECIES: Young of other skink species in Oklahoma, except the Great Plains Skink, are the same size as an adult Little Brown Skink, but have pale stripes on the body and a blue tail. Young of the Great Plains Skink are coal black and have white spots around the mouth and a blue tail. A Southern Coal Skink has dark dorsolateral stripes bordered on either side by a light stripe. The adult Little Brown Skink is much smaller than other adult skinks. This skink has a thinner body build than other skinks.

FOOD: Insects, spiders, and earthworms.

HABITAT: Woodlands, mainly on the forest floor.

REMARKS: The Little Brown Skink is unique in having a transparent disk in the lower eyelid through which it can see when the eye is closed; probably an adaptation for burrowing in soil or leaf litter. This diurnal lizard does not often bask in the open where it is visible to an observer. It is secretive, and often found in leaf litter or other secluded spots, and usually does not climb onto objects like rocks. This lizard frequently moves and can be heard as it moves about the dry leaves. When frightened this skink will not hesitate to jump into water to escape. If grabbed, this species will autotomize its tail. The tail then thrashes about, attracts the attention of the predator, and the lizard runs away. The common name of this species used to be the Ground Skink. The scientific name *Scincella* means little lizard and *lateralis* is a reference to the dark stripes down the sides of the body.

LIZARDS

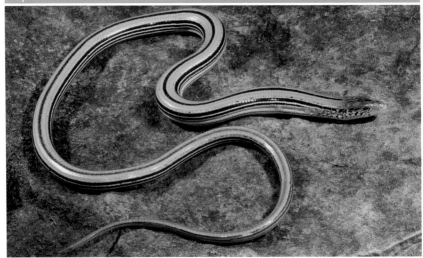

Junenile

SIZE: 22-42 inches.

APPEARANCE: This legless lizard has a tan to gold back with dark stripes down the midline and sides. There is a distinct groove that runs down the length of the body on each side. The belly is white. Most of its body is tail (up to 5/7 of its length). Many specimens are missing part of the tail. Like other lizards, glass lizards have eyelids and small ear openings.

SIMILAR SPECIES: A snake lacks ear openings and cannot blink. Other lizards have legs.

FOOD: Insects, lizards, spiders, snails, baby mice, and small eggs.

HABITAT: Grasslands, open woods, or in power line cuts through woods.

REMARKS: The tail may be easily autotomized during attempted capture. The wiggling tail distracts predators, allowing the lizard to escape. A new tail is later grown, but is never as long or as patterned as the original. One myth says that if you chop the lizard up, each segment will become a new lizard. Obviously, this is not so. The groove along the side of the body allows expansion of the body, which is important during feeding, when the female is carrying eggs, during movement, and in deep breathing. Larval ticks sometimes get into this groove and feed on the lizard. This secretive lizard burrows and is not often seen even where it is common. Western Slender Glass Lizards may be found on roads at dusk or after a rain. The female attends her eggs and does not abandon them. In captivity, a Western Slender Glass Lizard often spends time sitting in its water bowl with only its head out of water. Therefore, captives should be given a large enough water bowl to accommodate the whole lizard. The name *Ophisaurus* translates as "snake lizard" and *attenuatus* means slender.

Mediterranean Gecko
Hemidactylus turcicus

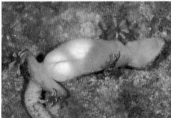
Belly of gravid female showing eggs

SIZE: 4 - 5 inches.

APPEARANCE: The body ground color is pale. The dorsal surface is covered with dark spots and bumpy projections. The toe pads are visibly enlarged. The tail is usually plump. It has large eyes, vertical pupils, and no eyelids. The skin is thin and on the belly it is translucent. If a female is carrying eggs (usually two), they will be visible through the skin on the underside of the lizard.

SIMILAR SPECIES: None in Oklahoma.

FOOD: Small insects and spiders.

HABITAT: In Oklahoma, it is found in association with buildings. In warm weather it moves outside and in cold weather it moves into buildings.

REMARKS: This species is not native to the United States, but it originated in the Mediterranean area and has moved throughout the world with humans. It has been expanding its range in the United States as adults or eggs are inadvertently or intentionally transported to new locations. Because of the unique habitat use of this lizard, it appears that its introduction into Oklahoma has not had an adverse effect on any native reptiles in the state. This lizard has a voice and can make soft squeaking sounds. Males may make a clicking sound. If captured, this lizard will readily autotomize its tail. Its toe pads, which are covered with microscopic hairs or setae, allow it to climb vertical surfaces and ceilings. It is nocturnal. It was introduced to the OU campus (Cleveland Co.) in the 1960s. Later, it was introduced on the OBU campus (Pottawatomie Co.), the OU Biological Station (Marshall Co.), Blaine, Garfield, Payne, Cherokee, and Oklahoma Counties. This species has temperature dependent sex determination.

LIZARDS

139

Snakes (Order Squamata)

BEHAVIOR

Snakes are carnivorous and as a group, eat a wide variety of rodents, reptiles, amphibians, fish, and invertebrates, but certain individuals or species can be quite particular about what they eat. Snakes employ the following methods to find prey: they may hunt for prey in the water, trail prey into burrows, sit and wait for prey to come by, or climb into trees after prey.

Snake behavior and locomotion are influenced by temperature. A cold snake is very sluggish and may be more apt to bite when pestered than a warm snake. When temperatures drop, snakes seek a protective shelter.

ANATOMY

Snakes have no external ear openings and no eyelids. They do have a clear covering (spectacle) over each eye, which is shed when the snake sheds its skin. Before a snake sheds, its skin gets an opaque or "milky" appearance and the eyes turn bluish-white. At this time the snake's vision is impaired. When this occurs, snakes may not eat and may be more temperamental than normal. This milky appearance lasts a few days and then partially clears up before the snake sheds its skin several days later.

Snakes may shed their skin several times a year. It was once believed rattlesnakes could be aged by counting rattle segments, but rattlesnakes add a new rattle segment each time they shed and cannot be aged accurately that way.

Depending upon the species, snake scales may be smooth, weakly keeled, or keeled (see Figs. 12a and 12b.) A keel is a thin ridge that runs along the midline of each scale. The scale immediately in front of a snake's vent is called the anal plate. In some snake species it is a single scale and in others it is divided (see Figs. 13a and 13b). The presence and number of certain scales on the head, such as upper labial scales, can be used to distinguish some species (see Figs. 15a, 15b and 15c.)

Snakes are unique because they can stretch their jaws very wide when eating. Snakes can also move the right and left sides of the jaw independent of the other side. Since snakes swallow their prey whole, this allows them to eat larger prey than would otherwise be possible. All snakes periodically replace their teeth.

REPRODUCTION

The mating process (or courtship) begins in the warmer months with the males seeking out possible mates. An encounter with another male of the species may result in confrontation, but it is rarely fatal. After the male has found a possible mate there is a ritualized courtship "dance" where the two snakes wrap around one another and begin mating. This courtship process can range from a few hours to a couple of days.

The majority of snake species lay eggs. The remaining species give birth to live young. Once the baby snakes hatch or are born, they are fully capable of self-care and are not dependent upon adults. In some cases, adults will protect neonates for a few days before leaving them.

CONSERVATION

Many people have an irrational fear of snakes (ophidiophobia.) Most of our snakes are harmless and actually benefit humans. Some farmers encourage snakes to live near stored grain because they help to reduce rodent populations. An untrue notion is that water snakes take game fish from the population and reduce the number available to fishermen. Snakes primarily remove sick and injured fish from the population, a practice that actually improves fish populations. As long as habitat is not destroyed, Oklahoma snakes should do well. Chemicals that kill snake prey could have a negative impact on snake populations. Feral and domestic free-roaming cats also kill numerous snakes.

IS IT VENOMOUS?

A popular misconception is, "if it rattles, it's a rattlesnake." Rattlesnakes do not always rattle and many non-venomous snakes make rattling noises by vibrating their tails rapidly when irritated. If they are in dry grass or leaves it sounds like a rattle. All venomous snakes in Oklahoma have triangular-shaped heads that are wider than their necks compared to Oklahoma's non-venomous snakes. The eyes of venomous species have cat-like, vertical-slit pupils, and the eyes of non-venomous snakes have round pupils (see Figs. 14a and 14b.) All of Oklahoma's venomous snakes have a single row of scales under the tail. Most other snakes have a double row of scales under the tail.

The best way to avoid an unpleasant encounter with a venomous snake is to know the habitats in which they are likely to occur and to be careful when in those areas. When hiking, watch where you put your hands and feet, especially when stepping over logs or rocks or around cliff areas. In southern and eastern Oklahoma, in areas near water, avoid going under bushes and small shrubs overhanging the water and look before you step near the banks. Our venomous snakes are not overly aggressive and if you avoid stepping on or near them you should have no problem. Venomous snakes should never be disturbed or handled, even if they appear dead. A recently killed individual may still have reflex actions that could result in a fang penetrating a person's skin.

The amount of venom injected in a strike is variable. Occasionally pit vipers give a "dry" bite in which no venom is injected. Even a freshly milked snake has venom and can inject it. If a venomous snake breaks a fang the broken fang is replaced with a new one.

Fortunately for most of us, the majority of people who are bitten by venomous snakes (envenomated) are people who intentionally handle these snakes. These include zoo keepers, professional herpetologists, people in snake-handling churches, individuals who keep venomous snakes as pets, and participants at rattlesnake round-ups.

GROUPS OF SNAKES

There are three groups of snakes in Oklahoma. The threadsnakes are small snakes with stubby heads and tails. These snakes cannot see and previously were called blind snakes. Threadsnakes eat termites and larval or pupal ants. Some threadsnakes can sense the chemical trail left by termites and follow it back to the nest. Some threadsnake species emit an odor, which enables them to enter termite nests without attack.

Non-venomous snakes are relatively harmless to humans, although some of the rear-fanged species subdue prey with a venom that they chew into the prey. This venom is harmless to most humans, although some people have an allergic reaction to it. Non-venomous snakes may bite if cornered or picked up, but none can seriously injure a human. A typical bite from a medium-to-large sized non-venomous snake normally results in the loss of only a few drops of blood. Often they do not break the skin when they bite. A more noxious defense is the emission of musk, which is often mixed with feces. Some small snakes, like the Ring-necked Snake and gartersnakes, can emit an incredibly pungent musk, which is hard to wash off. The relationships among the non-venomous snake species are being actively researched. Many biologists feel that this group should be split into several groups.

The pit vipers have heat-sensing pits between (but below) the eye and the nostril (see Fig. 14b.) These organs can detect warm prey with great accuracy and allow the viper to pin-point the position of potential prey. Rattlesnakes shed their skin two to four times per year and add a rattle each time they shed. Therefore, the number of rattles cannot be used to age snakes. Although it is possible for an old snake to have a large number of rattle segments, this is rarely seen because the rattle segments break off as the snake moves about over rocks and in vegetation. The curved fangs of pit vipers are located in the front part of the mouth. The fangs can move independently and are not fixed. When not in use they are folded up next to the roof of the mouth. During a strike, the fangs swing forward. When the snake strikes its prey, venom is released from the venom gland, flows through the hollow fang, and enters the prey. The snake then backs away and waits for the venom to take effect. Contrary to popular belief, Cottonmouths can and do bite underwater. This makes sense given that they eat fish.

All Oklahoma pit vipers give birth to live young. The females retain eggs in their bodies until time for hatching. This allows the helpless eggs to be protected and allows the mother to keep the eggs at an optimal temperature for development.

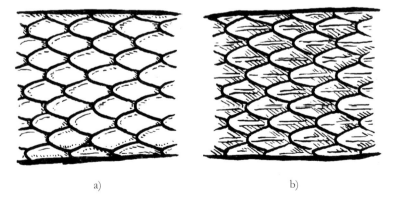

a)   b)

FIG. 12. - Comparison of snake scales: a) smooth scales; b) keeled scales

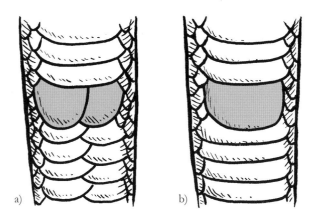

FIG. 13. - Snake anal plate: a) divided; b) single. Note: ventral scales overlap in direction of the tail

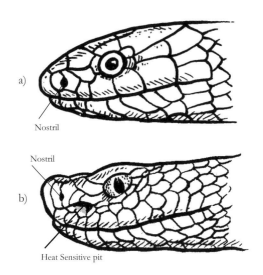

Nostril

Nostril

Heat Sensitive pit

FIG. 14. - (a) Snake head of generic, non-venomous snake. Note round pupil of eye and lack of heat sensitive pit; (b) Snake head of generic venomous snake. Note elliptical, vertical pupil of eye and heat sensitive pit

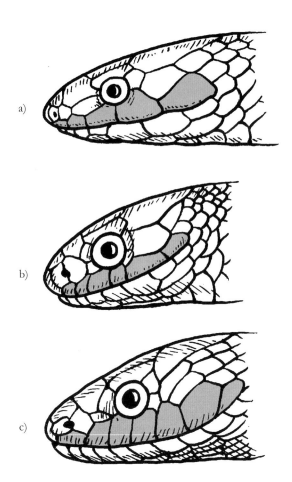

FIG. 15. - Upper-labial scale variations found in non-venomous snakes: a) 5 upper-labial scales; b) 6 upper-labial scales; c) 7 upper-labial scales

At the time of this printing, (2011) there is a website with additional information and photos about Oklahoma's snakes: **www.oksnakes.org**

New Mexico Threadsnake
Leptotyphlops dissectus

New Mexico Threadsnake

Plains Threadsnake

SIZE: 5-10 inches.

APPEARANCE: This smooth, shiny snake lacks an obvious neck and resembles a worm. Its head and tail end look similar, but the tail has a short spine. Its eyes are hidden under a scale. The tiny belly and dorsal scales are equal in size. Its back is pink, tan, red, or brown. Its belly is plain white or pink. The body often has an iridescent quality.

SIMILAR SPECIES: The New Mexico Threadsnake has two supralabial scales and the Plains Threadsnake has one (see diagram).

FOOD: Eggs, larvae, pupae and adults of termites and ants.

HABITAT: Prairies, hillsides, and semiarid regions with moist, loose soil for burrowing.

REMARKS: This snake is active in the evening and most likely encountered after a rain. Threadsnakes follow odor trails to locate other threadsnakes and prey. When disturbed, this snake tilts its scales, giving it a silvery look. If pestered, it coils into a ball, defecates, and excretes a foul, clear fluid from the vent. If handled, it may poke its tail into the handler or go limp. This snake is sometimes found in screech owl nests, after it presumably escaped being eaten. Invertebrates in the nest provide food for the snake, which in turn keeps invertebrates from bothering the babies. Owl chicks in nests with threadsnakes grow faster and have lower mortality than those without snakes. The upper jaw of the threadsnake is longer than the lower jaw, which enables the snake to avoid getting dirt in its mouth when it burrows. The female guards her eggs. These snakes used to be called blind snakes. The name *Leptotyphlops* means slender with blind eyes. Some scientists believe this snake should be in the genus *Rena*, making the scientific name *Rena dissecta* (See p. 4).

(See p. 4)

SNAKES

Plains Threadsnake
Leptotyphlops dulcis dulcis

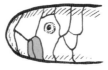

New Mexico Threadsnake

Plains Threadsnake

SIZE: 5-10 inches.

APPEARANCE: This smooth, shiny snake lacks an obvious neck and resembles a worm. Its head and tail end look similar, but the tail has a short spine. Its eyes are hidden under a scale. The tiny belly and dorsal scales are equal in size. Its back is pink, tan, red, or brown. Its belly is plain white or pink. The body often has an iridescent quality.

SIMILAR SPECIES: The New Mexico Threadsnake has two supralabial scales and the Plains Threadsnake has one (see diagram).

FOOD: Eggs, larvae, pupae, and adults of termites and ants.

HABITAT: Prairies, hillsides, and semiarid regions with moist, loose soil for burrowing.

REMARKS: This snake is active in the evening and most likely encountered after a rain. Threadsnakes follow odor trails to locate other threadsnakes and prey. When disturbed, this snake tilts its scales, giving it a silvery look. If pestered, it coils into a ball, defecates, and excretes a foul, clear fluid from the vent. If handled, it may poke its tail into the handler or go limp. This snake is sometimes found in screech owl nests, after it presumably escaped being eaten. Invertebrates in the nest provide food for the snake, which in turn keeps invertebrates from bothering the babies. Owl chicks in nests with threadsnakes grow faster and have lower mortality than those without snakes. The upper jaw of the threadsnake is longer than the lower jaw, which enables the snake to avoid getting dirt in its mouth when it burrows. The female guards her eggs. These snakes used to be called blind snakes. The name *Leptotyphlops* means slender with blind eyes. Some scientists believe this snake should be in the genus *Rena*, making the scientific name *Rena dulcis dulcis* (See p. 4).

Kansas Glossy Snake
Arizona elegans elegans

Color variation in a juvenile

SIZE: 27-36 inches.

APPEARANCE: It has smooth, glossy scales (see Fig. 12a) and a light brown or off-white ground color. There are 50 or more mid-dorsal brown blotches with dark outlines. Smaller blotches alternating with the dorsal blotches occur on both sides. The belly is unmarked and whitish. The anal plate is single (see Fig.13b.) There is a dark line running from the jaw to the rear of the eye and usually across the top of the head connecting the two eyes. The head is not much wider than the neck. The male has a slightly longer tail than a female of the same size.

SIMILAR SPECIES: A Bullsnake or a ratsnake has keeled scales. A kingsnake has a patterned belly. A ratsnake has a patterned belly and divided anal plates.

FOOD: Lizards, rodents, and chicks of ground-nesting birds. Rodents make up the bulk of the diet of this snake in Kansas and likely do in Oklahoma.

HABITAT: Sandy, open areas.

REMARKS: This species has a mild disposition and if handled may try to flail, but won't try to bite. This snake is active in the evening and at night. It spends its days under rocks or in burrows. The upper jaw is longer than the lower jaw, which is an adaptation to prevent dirt from getting in its mouth while it is burrowing. When disturbed, the snake produces a rattling sound by vibrating the tail against the ground or dried vegetation. This species constricts its prey. The female lays eggs. The name *elegans* refers to the elegant color pattern of this snake.

Darker color variant

SIZE: 8-11 inches.

APPEARANCE: This snake has smooth (see Fig. 12a), glossy black or dark gray dorsal scales. The head is narrow and the neck is thick. The body is muscular for burrowing. There is a pink to red unpatterned belly. The belly color extends to the third scale row on each side. The male has a longer tail than the female, but the female grows to a longer overall body size. The tail terminates in a hard, pointed tip that is harmless.

SIMILAR SPECIES: Other small snakes have keeled scales and lack a red belly color extending up the side. A Red-bellied Snake has keeled scales and a brown back. The red belly color on the Red-bellied, Flat Headed, and Black-headed Snakes does not go up to the third scale row on the side.

FOOD: Earthworms and possibly insects with soft bodies.

HABITAT: Damp, protected areas on wooded hillsides and along stream valleys. This snake often burrows into loose soil. Usually it is found under logs or flat rocks.

REMARKS: This docile snake is too small to bite humans. When handled it may press the tail with its pointed tip into the handler or it may smear musk and feces on the handler. It is secretive and normally encountered only in the spring when the soil is damp. When the weather is hot and dry, this snake moves underground along with the earthworms. The Western Wormsnake is an egg layer and may be locally abundant. This snake is rear fanged, but because of its small head size, poses no threat to humans. The name *vermis* means worm.

Close-up of head

SIZE: 14-20 inches.

APPEARANCE: This snake has large, red, dorsal blotches surrounded by thin black bands on a white to gray ground color. The red blotches do not cross onto the belly. Red and white areas often contain black dots in an older snake. The head has a strongly pointed snout. The top of the head is red with a black line just behind the eyes. The belly is plain white to cream colored. Scales are smooth (see Fig. 12a.)

SIMILAR SPECIES: A Milksnake has a patterned belly. The largest dorsal bands of the Texas Long-nosed Snake are black.

FOOD: Prefers reptile eggs, but may eat small snakes, mice, or lizards.

HABITAT: Sandy or loamy forested areas in which it can burrow, but is also found on open grass covered hillsides, usually near a wooded edge.

REMARKS: It is nocturnal, a good burrower, lives underground, and is rarely encountered. The best time to find this snake is in late spring, especially after heavy rains. It is very docile and never bites but does poorly in captivity because of its specialized diet of lizard and snake eggs. This snake has enlarged teeth on the upper jaw for slicing open eggs. It constricts its other prey. The female lays eggs. A juvenile looks similar to an adult, but the dorsal red blotches are smaller and pink. The name *coccinea* means scarlet. In Oklahoma, this is a Species of Special Concern and should not be taken from the wild.

SNAKES

Southern Black Racer

Eastern Yellow-bellied Racer

Color variation in Eastern Yellow-bellied Racer

SIZE: 36-60 inches.

APPEARANCE: The adult is long and slender-bodied. The scales are smooth (see Fig. 12a.) A juvenile has large mid-dorsal brown blotches and small brown or black spots on the sides. The juvenile has a tan or gray ground color. The pattern fades by the time the snake is several years old. The adult female attains a longer length than the male, but the male has a longer tail. The adult Yellow-bellied Racer has a plain brown to olive back with dark colored skin between the scales, making the scales look as though they were outlined in black. The unpatterned belly is yellow to cream. Hatchling Yellow-bellied Racers have dark edged blotches. The adult Southern Black Racer has a black to blue-black back, white upper and lower lips, and a light blue to cream unpatterned belly.

SIMILAR SPECIES: A ratsnake has weakly keeled scales. An adult Coachwhip does not have a solid body color. A young Coachwhip has mid-dorsal irregular bands rather than blotches. A dead Northern Rough Greensnake is dark blue (like the Southern Black Racer) but has keeled scales.

FOOD: Snakes, lizards, frogs, rodents, birds, and insects. Insects make up over 80% of the diet of both juvenile and adult Yellow-bellied Racers.

HABITAT: Found in a variety of relatively open habitats, especially grasslands and weedy fields. In eastern Oklahoma, it is common in open areas near woodlands and can climb quite high into trees.

REMARKS: This diurnal snake forages with its head up high using its acute vision to hunt. When disturbed, it rapidly vibrates its tail. If it is on dry leaves this sounds like a rattle. Although normally found on the ground, it may climb into trees and shrubs, hide under vegetation, or hide in mammal burrows to escape predators. This species is attracted to run-down buildings and barns, where debris on the ground provides cover objects. If captured, it will bite repeatedly, release musk, and thrash about. This snake does not do well in captivity. Several females may lay their eggs in the same nest. The eggs have a rough, bumpy texture. This snake is alert and can move very fast, hence the name Racer. *Coluber* means snake. Although the species name is *constrictor*, it does not constrict its prey.

SUBSPECIES: Eastern Yellow-bellied Racer, *Coluber constrictor flaviventris*, statewide except the Coastal Plain region of Oklahoma and the eastern 1/4 of Oklahoma counties; Southern Black Racer, *Coluber constrictor priapus*, Coastal Plain region of Oklahoma and the eastern 1/4 of Oklahoma counties.

Hatchling Eastern Yellow-bellied Racer

Prairie Ring-necked Snake

Mississippi Ring-necked Snake

Prairie Ring-necked Snake belly

152

SIZE: 10-14 inches.

APPEARANCE: It has a black or gray back with smooth scales (see Fig. 12a) and a gold belly with numerous dark spots. There is a bright gold or orange ring on the neck. The underside of the tail is usually red-orange. The female attains a larger body size than the male. The Prairie Ring-necked Snake has many irregularly spaced black spots on the belly. The anterior part of the belly is gold and the posterior part is reddish-orange. The Mississippi Ring-necked Snake has a yellow belly and a double row of black spots situated toward the midline of the belly. The neck ring of the Mississippi Ring-necked Snake is narrow and usually interrupted on the top of the neck.

SIMILAR SPECIES: Most small snake species lack a gold ring around the neck. A young Texas Brownsnake has a plain belly and keeled scales. The Northern Red-bellied Snake may have a tan to gold neck ring, but has a red belly and keeled scales.

FOOD: Earthworms and soft-bodied insects; also small salamanders where available.

HABITAT: Moist areas under logs, rocks, and debris. Frequently observed on rocky hillsides in wooded areas, but also commonly found in rocky grassland areas.

REMARKS: This little snake will coil its tail, exposing the bright underside if disturbed. This warns predators that it tastes bad. If handled, it frequently emits a foul-smelling musk that is hard to wash off. It makes a poor pet because it does not eat well in captivity. It is secretive and rarely found out in the open. This snake is gregarious and sometimes found in large numbers under a single rock or log, especially in the spring. This species is rear fanged, but uses its toxin to paralyze small prey and is no threat to humans. The female lays a small clutch of 5 or fewer eggs inside moist, rotting logs or other moist areas and often several females lay eggs in the same spot. Ring-necked Snakes have been found moving about in caves in the winter. *Diadophis* translates as the snake with a crown, probably in reference to the ring, and the name *punctatus* means spotted.

SUBSPECIES: Prairie Ring-necked Snake (*Diadophis punctatus arnyi*), statewide except southern McCurtain County; Mississippi Ring-necked Snake (*Diadophis punctatus stictogenys*), southern McCurtain County.

Defensive display in a Prairie Ring-necked Snake

Adult

Juvenile

SIZE: 24-36 inches.

APPEARANCE: The head has a V or spear point mark leading to the neck. The front end of the V sits between the eyes. The dark eye stripe extends through the eyes, goes past the mouth onto the neck, and has a dark outline. Large brown blotches extend down the midline of the back. On each side there are two rows of smaller blotches. The ground color is gray to light brown. The scales are slightly keeled and the anal plate is divided (see Fig. 12b and Fig. 13a.) The white belly has a double row of black squarish blotches. The underside of the tail has longitudinal stripes. A cross section of the body is shaped like a loaf of bread.

SIMILAR SPECIES: A Bullsnake has scales with distinct keels and a single anal plate. The Black Ratsnake lacks a spear point mark on the head and the dark face stripe stops at the mouth and does not extend onto the neck. The Kansas Glossy Snake and kingsnakes have smooth scales and a single anal plate.

FOOD: Rodents, birds, frogs, and bats.

HABITAT: Near waterways, in canyons, barnyards, or abandoned houses.

REMARKS: This snake is nocturnal. It gracefully climbs trees and buildings. When disturbed, this snake "rattles" its tail by vibrating it rapidly against the ground or dried leaves. If cornered it will coil up, strike, and sometimes hiss. Most individuals adapt well to captivity. This snake constricts its prey. It is valuable in controlling mouse and rat populations near houses and barns. The female lays 12 or fewer eggs in mid-summer that hatch about 2 months later. This snake is closely related to the cornsnake, which is popular in the pet trade. Some scientists believe this snake should be in the genus *Pantherophis* making the scientific name *Pantherophis emoryi* (See p. 4).

Adult color variation

Black Ratsnake

Texas Ratsnake

Texas Ratsnake hatchling

156

SIZE: 34-72 inches.

APPEARANCE: The back of this snake varies from plain black to pale with dark blotches. A dark stripe extends posterior from the eye, but stops at the mouth line. Light reddish colored skin between the scales is frequently visible. The belly, especially the anterior half, is light with white and black checkerboard markings. The posterior end of the belly is white with some dark mottling. The chin and throat are white or cream colored. The anal plate is divided (see Fig. 13a.) A cross section of the body is shaped like a loaf of bread. The scales are weakly keeled (see Fig. 12b.) On the young the back pattern is more boldly marked than in adults.

SIMILAR SPECIES: A Racer or a Coachwhip has smooth scales. The Great Plains Ratsnake has a spear point mark on the head, the dark face stripe extends past the mouth onto the neck, and there is striping under the tail. A watersnake has distinct keels on the scales. The Kansas Glossy Snake and kingsnakes have smooth scales and a single anal plate.

FOOD: Rodents, birds, eggs, and lizards.

HABITAT: Forests, fields, canyons, and farmlands.

REMARKS: This snake is an adept climber, and may climb trees to eat young squirrels and birds in their nests. During cool to warm weather it is diurnal; it is nocturnal in summer. It is also known as the pilot or chicken snake. It vibrates its tail when disturbed and this may sound like a rattle if the snake is on dry grass or leaves. Most ratsnakes tame down in captivity and often make nice pets. This snake constricts its prey. It is valuable in controlling mouse and rat populations around houses and barns. The female lays a clutch of 8-14 eggs in early to mid-summer that hatch about two months later. The Black Ratsnakes found along the Texas border and in the western ½ of Oklahoma are intergrades between the Texas Ratsnake (*Elaphe obsoleta lindheimeri*) and Black Ratsnake (*Elaphe obsoleta obsoleta*). These variable individuals have a yellow-brown background color and red around the distinct dorsal blotches. Some scientists believe this snake should be in the genus *Pantherophis* making the scientific name *Pantherophis obsoletus lindheimeri* and *Pantherophis obsoletus obsoletus* (See p. 4).

SUBSPECIES: Black Ratsnake (*Elaphe obsoleta obsoleta*), all of the Oklahoma range except along the Texas border; Texas Ratsnake (*Elaphe obsoleta lindheimeri*), along the Red River. There is a wide zone of intergrades between the two subspecies that runs through much of southern, central and western Oklahoma.

Hatchling Black Ratsnake

Western Mudsnake
Farancia abacura reinwardtii

SNAKES

SIZE: 38-54 inches.

APPEARANCE: It has a shiny black back with smooth scales (see Fig. 12a) and a red and black checkerboard belly. The head and neck are about the same width. The thickened pointed tail is almost like a spine.

SIMILAR SPECIES: No other Oklahoma snakes have a red and black belly.

FOOD: Mostly Amphiumas and sirens, but also may eat salamanders, tadpoles, frogs, and eels.

HABITAT: Swamps, sloughs, and mud-bottomed slow streams where there is abundant aquatic vegetation.

REMARKS: This snake is highly aquatic, eats food that is found in the water, and swims quite well. It is gentle but may poke at a captor with its pointed tail. The tail is particularly pointed in juveniles. The tail cannot sting and contrary to myth, it is not venomous. In reality, the tail tip is probed into a prey item to make it uncoil so it is easier to swallow. Another myth is that this snake can put its tail in its mouth, form a circle, and roll; hence the common name of hoop snake. This snake is nocturnal and spends most of its time burrowed under protective cover near the water and is rarely encountered. It does not do well in captivity because of its specialized diet. A female may stay with and guard her eggs. This snake is rear fanged, but poses no risk to humans. In Oklahoma, this is a Species of Special Concern and should not be taken from the wild.

Plains Hog-nosed Snake

Dusty Hog-nosed Snake

Juvenile Plains Hog-nosed Snake

SIZE: 16-25 inches.

APPEARANCE: Both subspecies of the Western Hog-nosed Snake have an upturned, pointed snout and a stout body. Its ground color varies from tan to brown, gray or yellow with dark oval blotches on its dorsum and smaller dark spots on the lateral part of its body. The scales are keeled (see Fig. 12b.) The belly has dark blotches, or may be all dark, and the underside of the tail is dark. The subspecies can be distinguished by counting the number of dark blotches between the head and the beginning of the tail. The Dusty Hog-nosed Snake has less than 32 blotches on the male and less than 37 on the female. The Plains Hog-nosed Snake has over 35 blotches on a male and over 40 on a female.

SIMILAR SPECIES: The Eastern Hog-nosed Snake is light colored on the underside of the tail.

FOOD: Toads, reptiles, reptile eggs, birds, and rodents. Lizards and lizard eggs comprise the bulk of the diet of Western Hog-nosed Snakes in Kansas and likely in Oklahoma, too.

HABITAT: Prairies with sand or gravel and flood plains. It prefers loose soil or sand.

REMARKS: This snake's defensive behavior includes hiding its head in its coils, spreading the head and neck, hissing, and feigning death by rolling belly up with its tongue hanging out of its mouth. Hog-nosed snakes will lie belly up for several minutes then flip over and crawl away. It rarely bites, but will threaten with false strikes. The displays of this inoffensive snake have earned it such names as "puff adder" and "hissing adder". Despite these names, it is not venomous to humans and poses no threat to humans. This snake has a good sense of smell, which is used to locate reptile eggs. This species spends a great deal of time underground and has a flap in the nostril that keeps dirt and sand out of the nose when it is burrowing. The Western Hog-nosed Snake is rear fanged, and its saliva, which is toxic to very small animals, is used to subdue its prey. The sharp fangs can be used to puncture an inflated toad so that it can be swallowed. (Toads tend to swell with air to appear larger than they really are and to prevent predators from swallowing them.) It is diurnal. The female lays a clutch of up to 20 eggs in mid-summer that hatch about two months later. Females may not lay egg clutches every year. The name *Heterodon* means that the teeth have different shapes, referring to the rear fangs and *nasicus* means having a pointed snout.

SUBSPECIES: Dusty Hog-nosed Snake (*Heterodon nasicus gloydi*), Bryan, Carter, and Johnston counties; Plains Hog-nosed Snake (*Heterodon nasicus nasicus*), western half of Oklahoma.

Head showing upturned snout for digging

Eastern Hog-nosed Snake
Heterodon platirhinos

Photos showing color variation

SIZE: 20-33 inches.

APPEARANCE: This snake has a pointed, upturned snout and a stout body. Its variable body color ranges from yellow to tan, gray, brown, or sometimes black. Some individuals are a plain dark color, others have dark squarish blotches on the back alternating with round spots on the sides. Even in plain individuals there is always a pair of large, dark blotches behind the head. The scales are keeled (see Fig. 12b.) The belly is usually mottled and the underside of the tail is lighter than the rest of the belly. A hatchling is strongly patterned.

SIMILAR SPECIES: The Western Hog-nosed Snake is dark on the underside of the tail.

FOOD: Toads, frogs, and salamanders; young eat insects.

HABITAT: Open, sandy areas, fields, and meadows. It prefers loose sand or soil.

REMARKS: If pestered, it inflates the neck and head, hisses and strikes. It may convulse, roll over, stick its tongue out, and feign death. It will emit musk and feces if pestered. This species virtually never bites, but it will pretend that it is going to bite. The displays of this inoffensive snake have earned it such names as "puff adder" and "hissing adder". Despite these names, it is not venomous to humans. Like the Western Hog-nosed Snake, this species is rear fanged and has saliva that is toxic to toads and frogs, but is no threat to humans. The rear fangs are used to bite into an inflated toad so that it deflates and can be swallowed. (Toads use inflation of the lungs to increase their size so they look larger and to make it hard for predators to swallow them.) This snake is diurnal. It is a burrower and spends a great deal of time underground. The female lays an average clutch of 25 eggs in mid-summer that hatch about two months later. The female may lay just a few eggs a day over multiple days or as many as 60 eggs at once. The scientific name *Heterodon* refers to the different shapes of the teeth (normal and fangs) in this snake's mouth and *platirhinos* means flat nose.

Juvenile

Eastern Hog-nosed Snake playing dead

163

Texas Nightsnake
Hypsiglena jani texana

SIZE: 12-16 inches.

APPEARANCE: This snake has smooth scales (see Fig. 12a) and a tan, brown, or grayish ground color with many brown to dark gray blotches on the back. It has a large, dark blotch on either side of the neck and a wide, long, mid-dorsal stripe on the back of its head and neck. A dark band extends from the eye back towards the neck. The belly is patternless and white or off-white. The pupil is vertical like that of venomous snakes (see Fig. 14b.) Belly and back scales are of similar size.

SIMILAR SPECIES: A young hog-nosed snake has a distinctly upturned snout. Young Massasaugas and Pygmy Rattlesnakes should have rattles and lack the two large blotches in the neck region.

FOOD: Lizards, frogs, insects, and threadsnakes. In captivity, large individuals may take small baby mice.

HABITAT: Arid and semiarid areas with sandy or rocky hillsides.

REMARKS: The nightsnake is rear fanged and has toxic saliva for subduing its prey, but is harmless to humans. When picked up, this snake writhes around, hisses, makes a popping sound with its cloaca, and secretes a foul liquid from its cloaca. This is smeared onto the person picking it up. This snake is nocturnal and may be seen crossing roads at night. The female lays a small clutch of about 4 to 8 eggs during the summer.

SNAKES

Hatchling

SIZE: 30-42 inches.

APPEARANCE: It has a tan or brownish dorsal color with around 60 dark blotches, edged with black, in a row down the middle of the back and smaller dark blotches alternating with the dorsal blotches along both sides. The spaces between the large blotches are about as big as the blotches. In some older individuals, the ground color darkens and obscures the blotches down the back. Young and most adults have a small rear-projecting spear point on the head. The belly is yellow to whitish with square, brown blotches. A Prairie Kingsnake has a single anal plate (see Fig. 13b.) The scales are smooth (see Fig. 12a.) The adult male is larger than the adult female.

SIMILAR SPECIES: A ratsnake or Bullsnake has keeled scales. A Milksnake is red, black, and white or cream banded. The Kansas Glossy Snake has a plain belly. A Massasauga has keeled scales, rattles on the tail, a triangular head, and nine plates on top of the head.

FOOD: Rodents, other snakes, lizards, and eggs. Mammals probably make up the bulk of the diet.

HABITAT: Open woodlands, prairies, and fields.

REMARKS: This snake eats non-venomous and venomous snakes and is not harmed if bitten by native venomous snakes. A kingsnake cannot be kept with other reptiles, or other Prairie Kingsnakes, because it will attempt to eat them. This snake is beneficial because it eats many rodents. This species constricts its prey. It is nocturnal, fairly docile, and rarely bites a captor. When disturbed it will vibrate its tail against the ground or fallen leaves, making a rattling sound, hiss, and often strike. This snake has coloration similar to that of the Massasauga and is frequently misidentified. Males may engage in combat to win females during the breeding season. The female lays 6-13 eggs. The word *calligaster* means beautiful belly in reference to the brown blotches on the light colored belly.

165

Color variation from the Ouachita Mountains

Color and pattern variation

166

SIZE: 36-48 inches.

APPEARANCE: The overall ground color of this snake is black. There is a white or yellow spot in each smooth (see Fig. 12a), black scale. Sometimes light spots form crossbands down the back. A juvenile has light spots on its sides and definite light crossbands that may form a pattern of light rings down the midline of the back. These crossbands tend to disappear with age. The belly is cream to yellowish with irregular shaped and spaced dark blotches. There is a single anal plate. An adult male grows larger and has a longer tail than an equal sized female.

SIMILAR SPECIES: A Black Ratsnake and baby racers lack spots on each scale. A Racer has a plain belly.

FOOD: Snakes, lizards, rodents, and birds.

HABITAT: Wetlands, woodlands, plains, and prairies usually near water and cover objects.

REMARKS: This diurnal snake becomes nocturnal during periods of extreme heat. The female lays a clutch of about 8 to 20 eggs in mid-summer that hatch about two months later. It eats venomous snakes and is uninjured by bites of native venomous snakes. The Speckled Kingsnake also consumes many watersnakes. A kingsnake cannot be kept with other reptiles because it will attempt to eat them. It is beneficial because it also eats large numbers of rodents. This snake constricts its prey. This snake is often called the "salt and pepper" snake. The Speckled Kingsnakes found in the Ouachita Mountains have more of a greenish tinge than other Speckled Kingsnakes in Oklahoma. Speckled Kingsnakes are in the eastern half of Oklahoma. The rest of Oklahoma supports intergrades between the Speckled Kingsnake and the Desert Kingsnake (*Lampropeltis getula splendida*) from Texas.

Speckled Kingsnake shedding

Red Milksnake

Color variation in Central Plains Milksnakes

Red Milksnake

SIZE: 16-28 inches.

APPEARANCE: The dorsal scales of this snake are smooth (see Fig. 12a.) There are dorsal red blotches outlined by black bands. The color between the black bands is white to yellow. The head and neck are about the same width. There is a single anal plate (see Fig. 13b.) The Red Milksnake has a red head with irregular black marks invading the red area. It usually has a whitish snout with black spots. There are 20 to 30 irregularly shaped dorsal red blotches that do not extend onto the belly and often some smaller black alternating blotches along the lower edge of each side. The belly is whitish with squarish black blotches. The Central Plains Milksnake has a black head with a whitish snout and 20 to 39 thin red bands that run onto its belly. The Louisiana Milksnake has 13 to 23 broad red bands that extend onto the belly and usually there is a non-patterned area down the midline of the belly between the red blotches. It has a dark head with a light nose area.

SIMILAR SPECIES: The Scarletsnake has a plain belly. A Prairie Kingsnake has brown blotches on its back and belly. The Texas Long-nosed Snake has broad black markings, a long nose, and a mostly plain belly.

FOOD: Rodents, snakes, and lizards.

HABITAT: Woodlands, rocky areas, open prairies, and fields.

REMARKS: This snake rarely basks, but it does raise its body temperature by sitting under warm rocks or other warm objects. During spring and fall it is diurnal, but it becomes nocturnal during the heat of summer. It may eat venomous snakes and is unharmed by their venom if bitten. A Milksnake constricts its prey. Contrary to myth, Milksnakes cannot milk cows and cannot digest milk. A Milksnake cannot be kept with other reptiles because it will attempt to eat them. It is beneficial because it eats large numbers of rodents. A Milksnake may hiss, rattle its tail, and strike when disturbed. The female lays 3-13 eggs. In Oklahoma, the Louisiana Milksnake is a Species of Special Concern and should not be taken from the wild.

SUBSPECIES: Red Milksnake (*Lampropeltis triangulum syspila*), eastern ½ of Oklahoma except extreme southeast; Central Plains Milksnake (*Lampropeltis triangulum gentilis*), Cimarron, Texas, Beckham, and Harmon Counties; and Louisiana Milksnake (*Lampropeltis triangulum amaura*), extreme southeastern Oklahoma.

Central Plains Milksnake

Western Coachwhip

Eastern Coachwhip

Western Coachwhip- red color variation

SIZE: 36-60 inches.

APPEARANCE: The Coachwhip has smooth scales (see Fig. 12a.) The scales and coloration on the tail of an adult Coachwhip make it look like a braided whip. The juvenile looks completely different than the adult and is boldly marked. It has a mottled pattern with dark, thin crossbands, especially on the anterior part of the body, and a long tail. The adult Eastern Coachwhip has a back that is dark anteriorly and light brown to reddish posteriorly. The belly usually varies with the dorsal ground color; the front half is dark and the back half is light, although some may have a uniform light colored belly. The adult Western Coachwhip either has a plain back or may have dark narrow, somewhat faded crossbands down the back. The ground color varies from light tan to dark brown to pinkish. The belly is cream to light gray and may have a double row of dark spots at the anterior end.

SIMILAR SPECIES: A Racer has a blue or yellow belly. A baby Racer has blotches on the back rather than thin crossbands. A ratsnake has weakly keeled scales.

FOOD: Insects, rodents, snakes, birds, and especially lizards.

HABITAT: Open woodlands and prairies; normally found in dry, sandy areas but occasionally found in moist areas.

REMARKS: This agile snake hunts with its head up and uses its good vision to locate prey. It is a very fast moving snake. A Coachwhip often chooses an erratic route when hunting and, if disturbed by humans, its erratic escape attempt may appear to be an attack on the human. If cornered, this snake will strike repeatedly and "rattle" its tail by vibrating the tail against leaves or the ground. If captured, this snake will writhe about in an attempt to escape and the tail appears to whip the captor. It will climb a tree or escape into a burrow when threatened. The female lays 7- 18 eggs. The name *Masticophis* means whip snake and *flagellum* means whip. Some scientists believe this snake should be in the genus *Coluber* making the scientific names *Coluber flagellum flagellum* and *Coluber flagellum testaceus* (See p. 4).

SUBSPECIES: Eastern Coachwhip (*Masticophis flagellum flagellum*), east of Interstate 35; Western Coachwhip (*Masticophis flagellum testaceus*), west of Interstate 35.

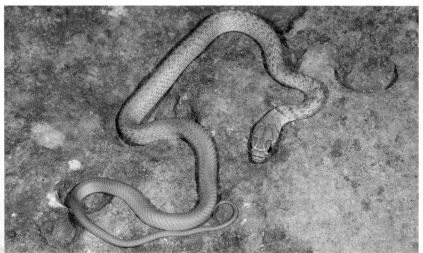

Hatchling Western Coachwhip

Yellow-bellied Watersnake

Blotched Watersnake

Yellow belly scales

SIZE: 30-48 inches.

APPEARANCE: The belly of this snake is cream to yellow, usually with dark tinting along the edge and sides of each belly scute. There is a divided anal plate and a double row of scales under the tail (see Fig. 13a.) The dorsal scales are strongly keeled (see Fig. 12b.) A fully grown female is longer than a fully grown male. The Blotched Watersnake has large, mid-dorsal, brown blotches alternating with small, squarish, brown blotches on the sides. Behind the head there are three or fewer dorsal blotches that line up and connect to the lateral squarish blotches, forming dark saddles. The ground color is tan to brown. The dorsal pattern may be obscured in dark colored adults. The adult Yellow-bellied Watersnake has a plain dark gray to dark greenish-brown back; some individuals may have a faded pattern similar to the Blotched Watersnake. A juvenile of either subspecies is boldly marked with dorsal blotches and squarish side blotches.

SIMILAR SPECIES: The Northern Watersnake has five or more dorsal blotches behind the head that line up and connect with the lateral squarish blotches to form saddle-like markings. The belly is normally strongly patterned. A Broad-banded, Midland, or Northern Diamond-backed Watersnake has a patterned belly and back. The Cottonmouth has vertical pupils, facial pits, a stouter body, a single anal plate, a single row of scales under the tail, and a shorter tail.

FOOD: Fish, frogs, tadpoles, salamanders, and crayfish.

HABITAT: Near semi-permanent to permanent bodies of quiet backwater.

REMARKS: This snake is generally active in the evening. It may bask from shrubs that hang over the water. This species is often killed by people who mistake it for a Cottonmouth. Cottonmouths often swim with most of the body on the surface of the water. Watersnakes usually swim with the head and neck out of the water and the rest of the body below the surface. To add to the confusion, some people refer to harmless watersnakes as water mocassins, a name sometimes used for Cottonmouths. Plain-bellied Watersnakes venture further from water than most watersnakes. A further problem for this species is that many fishermen think it eats mostly healthy game fish and reduces the population. In reality, watersnakes improve the quality of game fish populations by culling sick and injured fish. The female gives birth to live young. *Nerodia* refers to a fluid swimmer, *erythrogaster* means red belly, and *flavigaster* means yellow belly.

SUBSPECIES: Blotched Watersnake (*Nerodia erythrogaster transversa*), statewide except southeastern Oklahoma; Yellow-bellied Watersnake (*Nerodia erythrogaster flavigaster*), extreme southeastern Oklahoma.

Neonate Blotched Watersnake

SNAKES

SIZE: 22-36 inches.

APPEARANCE: The 11 to 17 wide, dark bands across the back of this snake are separated by much thinner yellow areas. The scales are keeled (see Fig. 12b.) Its yellow belly has distinct rectangular red to black markings that extend from the side to the midline. A dark band runs from the eye to the corner of mouth. Like all watersnakes, it has a double row of scales under the tail and a divided anal plate (see Fig. 13a.) The male has a longer tail than a female of equal length. A fully grown female is longer than a fully grown male.

SIMILAR SPECIES: A Cottonmouth is thick bodied, darker, has a wider head, vertical pupils, facial pits, a single anal plate, and a single scale row under the tail. The Northern Diamond-backed Watersnake, Yellow-bellied Watersnake, or Northern Watersnake all have thinner, more numerous crossbands on the back and lack a thick dark line behind the eye to the jaw.

FOOD: Young eat mostly fish and adults eat frogs, tadpoles, and fish.

HABITAT: Near a permanent source of water.

REMARKS: Normally this snake is nocturnal but may be encountered basking during the day and is likely to be active in cool weather during the day. It is non-venomous, but if harassed, will bite and emit an odoriferous musk to get free. Often it strikes as a defense mechanism, rather than to actually bite. It spends much of its time in water, and is often confused with the venomous Cottonmouth. This watersnake will flatten its head and body to appear larger, which somewhat resembles a Cottonmouth. Additionally, some people refer to harmless watersnakes as water mocassins, a name sometimes used for Cottonmouths. This snake is often thought to take only healthy game fish. In reality, watersnakes improve game fish populations by culling injured or sick individuals. The female gives birth to live young. *Nerodia* refers to a fluid swimmer, *fasciata* means banded, and *confluens* refers to the fact that the large dorsal blotches merge together.

SNAKES

Northern Diamond-backed Watersnake
Nerodia rhombifer rhombifer

SIZE: 30-48 inches.

APPEARANCE: This heavy-bodied snake has dorsal diamond-shaped light brown blotches separated by thin dark brown bands that form a chainlike pattern. The rectangular lateral blotch has two thinner lines (making a Y) that connect to adjacent dorsal blotches. This is especially obvious in the juvenile. The scales are heavily keeled mid-dorsally (see Fig. 12b.) The yellow belly may have half-moon marks on it, the largest of which are concentrated near the sides. There is a divided anal plate and a double row of scales under the tail (see Fig. 13a.) A male has raised bumps on the chin, which are used for courtship. A juvenile is boldly marked, but the pattern is the same as in the adult. A male has a longer tail than an equal sized female, but a full-grown female is larger than a full-grown male.

SIMILAR SPECIES: A Cottonmouth is darker, has vertical pupils, has facial pits, a single anal plate, and a single row of scales under the tail. The Broad-banded Watersnake has much broader dorsal bands. The Plain-bellied Watersnake lacks a belly pattern. Neither of these watersnakes has a chainlike dorsal pattern.

FOOD: Fish and frogs.

HABITAT: Near permanent, quiet backwaters. It especially likes areas with riprap.

REMARKS: This snake is diurnal except during very hot weather, when it becomes nocturnal. Occasionally it basks in trees. It is aggressive and will bite and emit musk when handled, but it is nonvenomous. Some people call harmless watersnakes water mocassins, a name sometimes used for Cottonmouths. Some fishermen fear this snake eats only healthy game fish. Actually, it helps improve game fish population quality by removing sick and injured fish. Mating balls of four or five males and one or two females have been observed in Sequoyah County. The female gives birth to live young. This snake hibernates in crayfish burrows. *Nerodia* means fluid swimmer and *rhombifer* refers to the rectangular blotches.

Northern Watersnake
Nerodia sipedon

Northern Watersnake

Midland Watersnake

Northern Watersnake belly- Note half-moon markings

SIZE: 22-42 inches.

APPEARANCE: The background color of this snake is dark brown to gray. At least the first five, or more, dorsal and lateral squarish blotches fuse to form crossbands or saddles on the anterior body. The thickest part of the dorsal crossband is at the mid-dorsal line. On the posterior part of the snake, the dorsal and lateral blotches alternate. In the adult the ground color frequently darkens to a dark brown and obscures the dorsal and lateral blotches. The scales are keeled (see Fig. 12b.) The belly is pale with dark brown to reddish half-moon shaped markings. These may be so faint as to be barely noticeable. A fully grown female is about three times heavier than a fully grown male. There is a divided anal plate and a double row of scales under the tail (see Fig. 13a.) A juvenile is boldly patterned and the dorsal and lateral blotches are quite distinct against the light ground color.

SIMILAR SPECIES: The Blotched Watersnake has a plain belly and has three or fewer dorsal blotches fused to lateral, squarish blotches to form a continuous saddle behind the head. The adult Cottonmouth has a less distinct pattern, weakly keeled scales, vertical pupils, facial pits, a stouter body with a shorter tail, a single anal plate, and a single row of scales under the tail. The Copperhead has vertical pupils, facial pits, crossbands with the thinnest portion of the crossband along the mid-dorsal line, a single anal plate, and a single row of scales under the tail.

FOOD: Frogs, small fish, salamanders, and crayfish.

HABITAT: Near any permanent source of water. Around lakes, it is common near riprap.

REMARKS: The Northern Watersnake will escape into water or vegetation if given the chance, but this pugnacious, non-venomous snake will strike and bite if cornered. In addition, it will musk and writhe about if handled. In the process the captor will get musk spread all over. Cottonmouths often swim with the head, neck, and back out of the water. Watersnakes usually swim with only the head and neck out of the water and the rest of the body below the surface. Both the Northern Watersnake and the Cottonmouth are aggressive, found near water, have similar color patterns (especially when the skin is dry), and often perch in vegetation overhanging the water. Because of its behavior people often think the Northern Watersnake is a Cottonmouth. To add to the confusion, some people refer to harmless watersnakes as being water mocassins, a name sometimes used for Cottonmouths. This species helps fishermen by culling sick or injured game fish, thus improving the game fish populations. The female gives birth to live young. *Nerodia* means fluid swimmer.

SUBSPECIES: Northern Watersnake (*Nerodia sipedon sipedon*), along the Kansas border; Midland Watersnake (*Nerodia sipedon pleuralis*), Southeastern Oklahoma. Many individuals in Oklahoma are probably intergrades between northern and midland watersnakes.

Neonate Northern Watersnake

SIZE: 20-32 inches.

APPEARANCE: This is a very thin snake with a plain green to yellowish-green back with keeled scales (see Fig. 12b.) Sometimes the chin is yellow. The tail is almost 40% of the total length of the snake. The belly is plain and white or light yellow. A male has a slightly longer tail than a female of the same length.

SIMILAR SPECIES: No other Oklahoma snake is slender and green with keeled scales.

FOOD: Spiders, crickets, grasshoppers, and caterpillars.

HABITAT: Trees, shrubs, or vines near water.

REMARKS: This snake is diurnal. It is commonly seen crossing roads or dead on the road in the fall, especially in the Ouachita Mountains. If seen dead, it will be dark blue rather than green. It hides in low trees or bushes. At night it can be found near the ends of branches in the tangle of leaves about four to five feet off the ground, often overhanging water. This snake will try to escape rather than bite when caught. It may even evade predators by entering the water. The female lays 3-10 eggs in early to mid-summer, which may be deposited in tree cavities. Hatchlings emerge in August and September. This snake may be declining because of the use of pesticides, which kill its prey. Unlike most snakes that eat relatively infrequently, this snake eats small meals almost every day. The scientific name *Opheodrys* means tree snake.

Bullsnake
Pituophis catenifer sayi

SIZE: 50-72 inches.

APPEARANCE: The Bullsnake has a yellowish-tan dorsal color and 41 or more dark blotches down the midline, which are usually darkest on the head, neck, and tail. The sides of the snake have many smaller dark blotches alternating with the dorsal blotches. Usually there is a dark line from the back corner of the mouth to the eye, which may continue across the head and connect the two eyes. There are dark vertical lines or bars between the scales on the upper lip. The tail has alternating dark and light vertical bands and the anal plate is single (see Fig. 13b.) The belly is yellow with dark spots. The scales are keeled (see Fig. 12b.)

SIMILAR SPECIES: The Kansas Glossy Snake has smooth scales and a plain belly. A ratsnake is usually darker, has weakly keeled scales, and a divided anal plate. A kingsnake has smooth scales. Rattlesnakes have triangular heads and rattles.

FOOD: Rodents, birds, and lizards. Rodents make up most of the diet, while birds and bird eggs make up a small percent of the diet.

HABITAT: Woodlands, fields, and shortgrass prairies.

REMARKS: This widespread snake is diurnal, except in hot weather. When disturbed it hisses, "rattles" its tail by vibrating it against dry vegetation, and may strike. This display is similar to that of a Prairie Rattlesnake, which may cause the Bullsnake to be misidentified as venomous. The Bullsnake finds prey by smell and often hunts in burrows. Normally it constricts prey, but if confined in a burrow, may squash prey against the burrow's side. One of Oklahoma's largest snakes, it often warms itself on a road in early morning or before dark. Because of this behavior, many are killed by vehicles. Also found in fields, many are killed by mowing or harvesting machines. The female lays eggs. Sometimes this snake is called a Gopher Snake. Previously the scientific name was *Pituophis melanoleucus sayi*. *Pituophis* means pine snake and *catenifer* means it has a chain-like pattern.

SNAKES

Belly

SIZE: 18-28 inches.

APPEARANCE: This snake has a brown to olive-brown back with keeled scales (see Fig. 12b.) There is a solid light stripe on the first three scale rows up from the belly. Between the pale stripe and the belly there is a dark line. There may be a wide, dark bordered, pale mid-dorsal stripe. The belly is usually plain cream to white, but may have a central row of dark spots, especially on the rear half. There is a divided anal plate and a double row of scales under the tail (see Fig. 13a.) A fully grown adult female is larger than a fully grown adult male. A young snake looks like an adult.

SIMILAR SPECIES: Gartersnakes have a bright mid-dorsal stripe and lack dark spots on the belly. The Lined Snake has a patterned belly. The Gulf Crayfish Snake has darker, shiny scales, a double row of half-moons on the belly, and the light stripe above the belly is only on scale rows one and two.

FOOD: Soft-bodied (molting) crayfish, sometimes frogs, and tadpoles.

HABITAT: Lakes, ponds, or slow moving waters with large crayfish populations.

REMARKS: When temperatures are moderate, this snake is active during the day, but when temperatures are high it becomes nocturnal. It likes to bask on limbs overhanging water and quickly drops into the water if approached. It retreats to and hibernates in crayfish burrows. If pestered, this snake will flatten out its body and emit musk. This is a docile snake and rarely bites, but it makes a poor pet because of its diet of molting crayfish. This species can be found in urban areas. The female gives birth to live young. *Regina* means queen.

SNAKES

SIZE: 14 - 24 inches.

APPEARANCE: This small snake is similar to a Graham's Crayfish Snake. The back is shiny and plain dark brown or olive brown. The light stripe on each side above the belly is only on scale row one. The scales are keeled (see Fig. 12b.) The light colored belly has two longitudinal rows of large half-moon shaped dark markings. There is a divided anal plate and a double row of scales under the tail (see Fig. 13a.) A young snake looks like an adult. A fully grown female is larger than a fully grown male. The tail of an adult male is longer than the tail of a female of the same length.

SIMILAR SPECIES: Gartersnakes and the Lined Snake have light lines on the back. The Graham's Crayfish Snake has the lateral stripe including the first three scale rows and does not have a double row of half-moons on the belly.

FOOD: Soft-bodied (molting) crayfish are its preferred food. It will also eat hard-shelled crayfish, small fish, frogs, and salamanders. Juveniles eat aquatic insects.

HABITAT: Mainly aquatic. Found in sluggish waters with muddy bottoms, under submerged logs and roots, and in floating aquatic vegetation.

REMARKS: Found very rarely in southeastern Oklahoma. The Gulf Crayfish Snake is very aquatic and secretive. It normally spends its days under a cover object near the water's edge or floating in aquatic vegetation. This species is very docile and rarely bites, but it does poorly in captivity because of its diet of molting crayfish. If approached, it will flatten out its body. If handled this snake will smear a foul musk on the handler. The female gives birth to live young. *Regina* means queen, *rigida* is a reference to the fact that this snake often feels stiff or rigid when handled, and *sinicola* indicates that it inhabits the Gulf region. This snake is an Oklahoma Species of Special Concern. It is protected by state law and cannot be removed from the wild.

SNAKES

181

Long-nosed Snake
Rhinocheilus lecontei

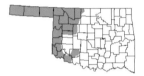

Elongated nose

SIZE: 22-32 inches.

APPEARANCE: The long head of this snake is black and a little wider than the neck. The pointed nose is red and has an elongate scale at the anterior tip. The back has red and black alternating blotches with yellow borders. The black blotches have yellow to white speckles and the red blotches have black speckles. The scales are smooth (see Fig. 12a.) The belly is yellow or white and usually plain but some individuals have dark spots. There is a single row of scales under the tail and a single anal plate (see Fig. 13b.)

SIMILAR SPECIES: A Milksnake has a definite belly pattern. The Scarletsnake has thin, black bands rather than black blotches. Both the Milksnake and Scarletsnake have a double row of scales under the tail.

FOOD: Lizards, lizard eggs, small snakes, small baby rodents, and some insects.

HABITAT: Prairies, weedy fields, and sandy or gravelly areas in river and creek valleys.

REMARKS: This snake is nocturnal and a good burrower. Its upper jaw is longer than the lower jaw and hangs over the shorter, lower jaw. This keeps dirt from getting into the snake's mouth while it is burrowing. It spends its day underground. It follows chemical trails left by lizards during the day to find the sleeping lizards at night. This snake constricts its prey. Occasionally when captured, this snake will coil its body, hide its head, and vibrate its tail. If the snake is on dried grass or leaves, the vibrating tail sounds like a rattle. Some individuals emit a fluid made of blood, feces, and musk when captured, but almost never bite. The female lays eggs. The name *Rhinocheilus* means nose lip, referring to the long nose. In Oklahoma, this is a Species of Special Concern and should not be taken from the wild.

SNAKES

Variable Groundsnake
Sonora semiannulata semiannulata

Groundsnake pattern variations

SIZE: 8-12 inches.

APPEARANCE: This is a small, smooth-scaled (see Fig. 12a) snake. The back pattern of this snake is highly variable and may be (1) plain brown or orange-brown, (2) brown or orange-brown with a mid-dorsal reddish line extending from the neck, (3) brown or orangish-brown with black crossbands in the neck region, or (4) brown or orange-brown with black crossbands spaced down the length of the body. The head is slightly wider than the neck. This snake has an unpatterned white or yellow belly. The underside of the tail may be plain or have faint crossbands.

SIMILAR SPECIES: The Flat-headed Snake has a flattened head and bright pink belly. An earthsnake or brownsnake has keeled scales.

FOOD: Scorpions, spiders, insects, and centipedes.

HABITAT: Open areas with sandy or clay loam soils, or sparsely wooded areas. This snake is often hidden.

REMARKS: The Variable Groundsnake is so variable that it is often difficult to identify, especially the plain colored individuals. This harmless snake is normally encountered in the spring and several may be found together under the same cover object. During late spring one year, as many as 60 were found on a single hillside in southern Oklahoma. This snake has nasal valves that keep dirt and debris from entering the respiratory tract. The rear teeth are grooved and may deliver a saliva that is toxic to invertebrates, but its small size makes this species no threat to humans. This species lays eggs. The hatchlings from a single clutch of eggs may have multiple color patterns, but at one time scientists thought that each of the color patterns was a different species or subspecies. We now know that all belong to the same species. The name *semiannulata* translates as half-ring in reference to the fact the rings on the back do not go onto the belly.

Adult color variations

SIZE: 9-13 inches.

APPEARANCE: This snake has a light tan to gray mid-dorsal stripe bordered on each side by pairs of dark spots. The ground color below the stripe varies from gray-brown to reddish-brown. Some individuals have thin, faded crossbands connecting the pairs of dorsal spots, especially in the eastern ¼ of Oklahoma. The sides of the body are darker than the mid-dorsal stripe. There is a dark spot under each eye and a black blotch on either side of the neck. There are seven upper labial scales (see Fig 15c) and some of these have dark markings. The scales are keeled (see Fig 12b.) The belly is plain yellow, brown, or pink. The lateral edge of the belly may have small, black dots. A fully grown adult female is larger than a fully grown male. The juvenile has a yellow band across the neck and a dark colored back.

SIMILAR SPECIES: A Ring-necked Snake has a strongly patterned belly and smooth scales. A groundsnake or wormsnake has smooth scales. An earthsnake lacks a dorsal pattern. The Red-bellied Snake has a red belly and a white patch under the eye. A Lined Snake has a pale lateral stripe and a patterned belly.

FOOD: Earthworms and slugs.

HABITAT: Under protective cover in urban areas, wetlands, and woodlands. It prefers damp, shaded areas inhabited by earthworms. It is often found in disturbed areas.

REMARKS: The Texas Brownsnake is diurnal in the spring and fall, but becomes nocturnal in the heat of the summer. When the weather is hot and dry, individuals may aggregate to reduce water loss. This snake is fairly common in urban areas, but rarely seen because of its secretive nature. If frightened, this snake may flatten its body and emit a mildly offensive musk. The female gives birth to live young. The name *texana* refers to Texas.

SNAKES

Red-bellied Snake
Storeria occipitomaculata

Color variations

Note plain red belly

SIZE: 8-12 inches.

APPEARANCE: The Red-bellied Snake has an unpatterned red or orange belly. The keeled, dorsal scales (see Fig. 12b) are rusty or gray. There is usually a pale, mid-dorsal line that may be gray, brown, or red and is bordered on both sides by thin, dark lines. The head is usually darker than the body. A fully grown female is larger than a fully grown male. The Northern Red-bellied Snake has three distinct light spots on the nape of the neck. The white spot under the eye has a black border next to the mouth. The Florida Red-bellied Snake has three spots that are usually fused to form a neck band. The white spot under the eye extends to the mouth.

SIMILAR SPECIES: A Ring-necked Snake has smooth scales and a patterned belly. The brownsnake lacks the red belly and has a dark blotch on each side of the neck. An earthsnake has a pointed nose and no light spots on the neck.

FOOD: Slugs, earthworms, and snails.

HABITAT: Woodlands especially moist hillsides with leaf litter and protective cover.

REMARKS: This little snake is rarely encountered because of its secretive nature. It is nocturnal. It will not bite and is totally harmless. If pestered it will emit a foul musk and sway its head back and forth while curling its upper lip. The female gives birth to live young. The name *occipitomaculata* means spots on the back of the head and *obscura* means that the spots are obscured, or in this case they run together.

SUBSPECIES: Northern Red-bellied Snake (*Storeria occipitomaculata occipitomaculata*), eastern tier of counties, except in coastal plain region of McCurtain County; Florida Red-bellied Snake (*Storeria occipitomaculata obscura*), coastal plain region of McCurtain County. The individuals in extreme southeastern Oklahoma may be intergrades of Northern and Florida Red-bellied Snakes.

SNAKES

185

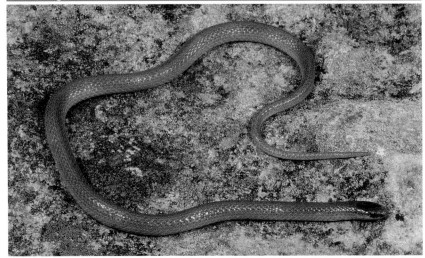

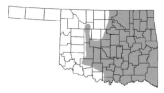

Pink belly

SIZE: 7-8 inches.

APPEARANCE: The Flat-headed Snake is a small snake with a patternless back that is tan, light brown, or reddish-brown. It has smooth scales (see Fig. 12a.) The head is slightly darker than the body and there are six upper labial scales (see Fig. 15b.) The belly is light pink to pinkish orange and may fade to light cream or white near the lateral edges of the belly. The male has a slightly longer tail than a female of equal length, but the adult female attains a greater overall length than the male.

SIMILAR SPECIES: The Plains Black-headed Snake normally has a noticeably darker head and seven upper labial scales. The dark coloration on the head tapers to a point on the neck. A Texas Brownsnake or a Red-bellied Snake has keeled scales. The Western Wormsnake has a pink belly that extends up onto the sides. An earthsnake has a white to yellowish belly. The threadsnake lacks distinct eyes and its tail is not tapered. A plain colored Variable Groundsnake has a white or yellowish belly.

FOOD: Insects, insect larvae, centipedes, spiders, and slugs.

HABITAT: Moist areas under rocks, logs, and debris. Rocky, prairie areas or woody hill-sides.

REMARKS: This snake is secretive and nocturnal. It is rear fanged but lacks a well-developed venom system and is of no threat to humans. This snake does not leave the protection of cover objects very often. During hot, dry weather and in the winter this snake moves under ground. This species lays eggs. The scientific name *Tantilla* means small and *gracilis* means graceful.

SNAKES

Plains Black-headed Snake
Tantilla nigriceps

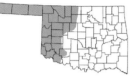

SIZE: 7-10 inches.

APPEARANCE: This small, unpatterned, brown or brownish-gray snake has a distinct dark color on its head extending onto the neck where the dark coloration tapers to a point. The scales are smooth (see Fig. 12a) and the belly is light cream to whitish with a narrow pink band down the midline. There are seven upper labial scales (see Fig. 15c.)

SIMILAR SPECIES: The Flat-headed Snake has six upper labial scales and lacks a black head. A Texas Brownsnake has keeled dorsal scales. An earthsnake or a plain colored Variable Groundsnake has a plain, white belly without a pink band down the midline. The threadsnake lacks distinct eyes and its tail is not tapered.

FOOD: Centipedes, spiders, and insect larvae.

HABITAT: Grasslands, sandhills, rocky canyons under rocks and debris, and in burrows where the soil is moist.

REMARKS: This species is rear fanged, but like the related Flat-headed Snake lacks a well-developed venom system. It is small and docile and poses no threat to humans. Its venom is used only on invertebrate prey and not as a defense. This species lays eggs. This snake can be fairly common in the spring under rocks in its preferred habitat. The Plains Black-headed Snake may be seen crossing the roads at night. *Tantilla* means small and *nigriceps* refers to the black head.

SIZE: 16-20 inches.

APPEARANCE: This snake has a black or brown dorsal color, which sometimes has an olive cast. There is a distinct yellow to orange mid-dorsal line that fades to cream or white near the tail. It has a light lateral line on scale rows two and three up from the belly. The line may have a wavy appearance. There is a large, triangular, black blotch on either side of the neck. The top of the head is lighter and usually grayer than the large, black, neck blotches. Dark side blotches are obvious near the head, but the blotches fuse to form a solid line about ⅓ of the way down the body or are reduced to dark spots that disappear near the tail end. There are dark vertical bars between the scales on the upper lip. The scales are keeled (see Fig, 12b.) The belly is plain and whitish to light greenish or gray.

SIMILAR SPECIES: A ribbonsnake lacks neck spots. Marcy's Checkered Gartersnake has a thinner, light lateral stripe near the head that sits only on the third scale row up from the belly; the black, neck blotches are elongate rather than triangular. An Eastern or Red-sided Gartersnake does not have the dark neck blotches.

FOOD: Adult amphibians, tadpoles, and small fish. Amphibians are the main prey item.

HABITAT: Flat, dry areas near a water source.

REMARKS: This snake will emit musk if captured, but it is not particularly aggressive and usually does not bite. In Oklahoma, this snake is found only in Cimarron County. A female gives birth to live young. During the hot summer months this diurnal snake becomes nocturnal. *Thamnophis* means a snake of small shrubs and bushes.

SNAKES

Neonate

SIZE: 18-24 inches.

APPEARANCE: This brown, olive, or tan snake has keeled scales (see Fig. 12b) and a mid-dorsal yellow stripe that usually has jagged edges. Below the mid-dorsal stripe on either side is a double row of alternating black squares that gives the snake an overall checkered appearance. On the second and third scale rows from the belly there is a pale line. Near the head this line includes only the third scale row. Below the light lateral stripe there is another row of black squares. There is a black, elongate blotch on either side of the neck. In front of each neck blotch is a cream to yellow crescent or curved band that is usually edged in black. There is a light dot on the top of the head. There are vertical black bars on the upper lip. The belly is unpatterned and cream to yellowish, but some of the belly scales may have dark edges.

SIMILAR SPECIES: Near the head the Western Black-necked Gartersnake has a light lateral stripe on scale rows two and three up from the belly. The Red-sided Gartersnake lacks a yellow curved band or triangle on each side of the head in front of the black blotch on the neck. The Plains Gartersnake has light lines on the third and fourth scale rows up from the belly on each side.

FOOD: Frogs, tadpoles, fish, crayfish, lizards, and earthworms. Amphibians are the favorite food of adults and earthworms are preferred by juveniles.

HABITAT: Dry grasslands near a source of water.

REMARKS: This species is diurnal, but it may be found active at night during the hot summer months. Although this snake may emit musk if captured, it is less likely to bite than most gartersnakes. The female gives birth to live young. *Thamnophis* means snake of small shrubs and bushes.

SNAKES

189

Orange-striped Ribbon Snake

Arid land Ribbon Snake

SIZE: 19-30 inches.

APPEARANCE: This long, thin snake is a close relative of the gartersnakes. It has keeled scales (see Fig. 12b) and a plain cream to gray belly. The back is brown or black with scattered flecks of white. There is a yellow or orange mid-dorsal stripe and on each side of the body there is a pale yellow or cream stripe on the third and fourth scale rows up from the belly. There are two fused yellow spots or a single spot on the top of the head. There is usually a small, white blotch both in front and behind each eye. The head of this snake is shorter than that of gartersnakes. The slender tail is ¼ to ⅓ of the entire body length.

SIMILAR SPECIES: A gartersnake has a tail less than ¼ of its total length and is thicker bodied than a ribbonsnake.

FOOD: It mainly eats amphibians, like small frogs and tadpoles, but also may ingest small fish

HABITAT: Near water, preferably with dense vegetation.

REMARKS: This diurnal snake may be observed basking near water. It will escape into the water or thick vegetation if threatened. If pestered it may strike and emit a foul musk. This snake is very alert and can move rapidly. During the heat of summer it may become nocturnal A female gives birth to live young. Most of the state has the Orange-striped Ribbonsnake, but in the western ⅙ of Oklahoma including the panhandle, the ribbonsnakes are intergrades between the Orange-striped Ribbonsnake and the Arid Land Ribbonsnake (*Thamnophis proximus diabolicus*). The intergrades have an overall lighter and duller ground color above the lateral stripe. The previous common name of this snake was the Western Ribbonsnake. *Thamnophis* means snake of small shrubs and bushes.

190

Adult

Hatchling

SIZE: 20-28 inches

APPEARANCE: The Plains Gartersnake has a mid-dorsal yellow or orange stripe and lateral light stripes on the third and fourth scale rows up from the belly. Between the lateral stripes and mid-dorsal stripe are two rows of alternating black squares. This gives the snake a checkerboard pattern. In dark individuals the black spots between the stripes may be hard to see. Below the lateral stripes is another row of black squares. The dorsal ground color is olive-gray or brown. There are black, vertical bars on the white, upper lip scales. There is a light spot on the top of the head. There is a black blotch on each side of the neck. The scales are keeled (see Fig. 12b). The belly is light with a row of black spots down each side. The tail of a male is longer than that of an equal sized female.

SIMILAR SPECIES: Most gartersnakes have light stripes on the second and/or third scale rows up from the belly, but not on the fourth scale row. A ribbonsnake does not have three rows of black squares on each side of the back and there are no black vertical bars on the lips.

FOOD: Amphibians, rodents, leeches, fish, insects, and earthworms. Amphibians make up the bulk of the diet.

HABITAT: In grasslands near a water source. This snake may use crayfish burrows as retreat sites.

REMARKS: This snake is diurnal. During cooler times of the year it is active at midday and during the hottest portion of the year it is active early and late in the day. It is less flighty than other gartersnakes but if pestered, it will emit a foul musk. The female gives birth to live young. *Thamnophis* means snake of small shrubs and bushes.

SNAKES

Red-sided Gartersnake

Eastern Gartersnake

Texas Gartersnake

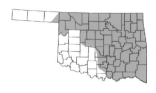

Intergrade of Red-sided Gartersnake X Texas Gartersnake

192

SIZE: 18-26 inches.

APPEARANCE: This species shows great individual variation in coloration. All three sub-species of the Common Gartersnake have a somewhat checkerboard appearance on their sides. Above the light lateral stripe there are two rows of alternating, dark blotches and below the light lateral stripe is another row of dark blotches. Above the lateral stripe the ground color between the squarish blotches may be dark, giving the snake the appearance of a wide, dark, dorsolateral stripe. In this case, only the black blotches below the lateral stripe are evident. All Common Gartersnakes have keeled scales (see Fig. 12b) and the belly is light colored with some dark spotting. The Eastern Gartersnake has a mid-dorsal yellow stripe and a pale lateral stripe on the second and third scale rows up from the belly. A double row of black blotches usually sits between the lateral and mid-dorsal stripes. The skin between the blotches is yellow or tan. The Red-sided Gartersnake has red or orange spots between the black blotches on its sides. The amount of red varies from almost none to very obvious, some individuals have red only on the skin between the scales. The mid-dorsal stripe is yellow to light orange. The lateral stripes are on scale rows two and three up from the belly. The Texas Gartersnake has a broad mid-dorsal orange stripe. The stripe down each side of the anterior ⅓ of the body is wide and includes scale rows three and parts of rows two and four. The skin between the dark blotches between the lateral and mid-dorsal stripes is white.

SIMILAR SPECIES: No other gartersnake has the red coloration. A Plains Gartersnake or a ribbonsnake has light lines on the third and fourth scale rows, not on row two. Marcy's Checkered Gartersnake has a yellow crescent or triangle on each side of the head in front of the black blotch on the neck.

FOOD: Amphibians, earthworms, fish, rodents, other reptiles, birds, and bird eggs. The bulk of the diet of adults consists of amphibians. Baby snakes eat mainly earthworms.

HABITAT: Found in many habitats, but normally near water.

REMARKS: This snake is diurnal. If approached this snake will first try to escape. If this doesn't work it will flatten out its head and the front part of the body exposing its red coloration by stretching its skin. This quick snake often bites or expels an unpleasant musk when first captured. This snake will autotomize its tail if the tail is grabbed by a predator. This species is likely to be one of the first snakes out in the spring. A female gives birth to live young. *Thamnophis* means snake of small shrubs and bushes. In Oklahoma, the Texas Gartersnake is a Species of Special Concern and should not be taken from the wild.

SUBSPECIES: Texas Gartersnake (*Thamnophis sirtalis annectens*), the northwestern part of the Oklahoma range. They have also been found on the south side of Rich Mountain in LeFlore County; Red-sided Gartersnake (*Thamnophis sirtalis parietalis*), central and eastern Oklahoma; part of the mid-portion of the state is probably an intergrade zone between the Texas and Red-sided Gartersnakes; Eastern Gartersnake (*Thamnophis sirtalis sirtalis*), a very thin strip along the southern ⅔ of the border between Arkansas and Oklahoma. Whether these different color morphs are ecomorphs of subspecies remains to be resolved.

Note pattern on belly

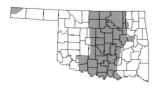

Variation in color

SIZE: 7.5-15 inches.

APPEARANCE: This small snake has a ground color of gray, tan, or light brown. There is a pale white, gray, or yellowish stripe down each side on scale rows two and three, and one down the midline. Above the two light side stripes there is usually an indistinct, dark, faded line or series of semi-connected dots. The head is somewhat pointed. The upper labial scales (see Fig. 15) are pale and have no markings. The belly is whitish to cream and has two rows of dark half-moon shaped blotches down the midline. The scales are keeled (see Fig. 12b.) An adult male has a longer tail than a comparably sized female.

SIMILAR SPECIES: A Gulf Crayfish Snake lacks a pale mid-dorsal line. Gartersnakes, the ribbonsnake and the Graham's Crayfish Snake lack the double row of half-moon markings on the belly. The brownsnake has a pair of dark blotches at the back of the head and dark markings on the upper labial scales.

FOOD: Earthworms.

HABITAT: Prairies, grasslands, thinly wooded areas, dump sites, and urban areas under protective cover.

REMARKS: This snake is nocturnal. It can be found in towns and cities in vacant lots and parks under debris. This species may be quite commonly found in late spring and early summer. More than 50 have been seen on a single hillside in late spring under habitat cover. When captured it may emit a foul-smelling musk, but rarely bites. Lined Snakes will burrow in loose soil or in matted grass. The female gives birth to live young. The name *lineatum* means lined.

Rough Earthsnake
Virginia striatula

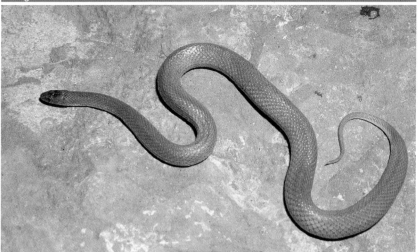

Adult color variations

SIZE: 7-10 inches.

APPEARANCE: This snake has a plain brown to reddish-brown back, keeled scales (see Fig. 12b) and a pointed nose that gives the head a cone-shaped appearance. The back of the head is only a bit wider than the neck. Young usually are darker and have a light band on the neck. There are five upper labial scales (see Fig. 15a.) The belly is off-white or yellow. The male has a longer tail than a female of the same length, but the female attains a greater overall length than the male.

SIMILAR SPECIES: A Smooth Earthsnake has smooth scales and six upper labial scales. The Ring-necked Snake has smooth scales, a gold neck ring, and a patterned belly. A worm-snake has smooth scales and a pink belly color that extends up to the third row of dorsal scales. The brownsnake has a thicker body and a dorsal color pattern. A Red-bellied Snake has six upper labials, three pale spots or a blotch on the back of the neck, and a dorsal color pattern rather than a plain back. The groundsnake usually has a dorsal color pattern and smooth scales. A Flat-headed Snake has smooth scales and a pale pink belly.

FOOD: Earthworms, slugs, snails, small frogs, and lizards.

HABITAT: Woodlands and suburban areas under protective cover. It prefers damp soil.

REMARKS: This is a secretive, nocturnal snake that rarely ventures far from protective cover. This snake does well in urban areas. Although it will not bite humans, it will release an odoriferous musk if pestered. Sometimes an individual will turn upside-down with its tongue hanging out and become rigid if pestered. The female gives birth to live young.

SNAKES

Adult color variations

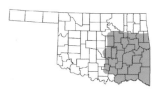

SIZE: 7-10 inches.

APPEARANCE: The Western Smooth Earthsnake has smooth scales anteriorly, but may have weakly keeled scales posteriorly (see Fig. 12b.) The dorsal ground color is reddish to grayish-brown. It usually has a faint light stripe down the mid-dorsal line that may be bordered with faded dark markings or dots, but some individuals are plain. Some individuals have a faint dark line between the eye and nostril. There are six upper labial scales (see Fig. 15b.) The belly is plain and white or yellowish. A male has a longer tail than a comparably sized female, but the female attains a greater overall length than the male.

SIMILAR SPECIES: A Ring-necked Snake has a patterned belly and ring around the neck. The wormsnake has a pink belly. A Rough Earthsnake has a cone-shaped head, keeled scales, and five upper labial scales. A brownsnake has keeled scales and seven upper labial scales. The Red-bellied Snake has keeled scales, a pale blotch or three pale spots on the neck, and a white lip patch. The dorsal color of a Flat-headed Snake is paler than that of the Western Smooth Earthsnake and it has smooth scales and a pink belly. The groundsnake has smooth scales and often has a pattern.

FOOD: Earthworms and soft-bodied invertebrates.

HABITAT: Moist woodlands, wooded urban areas, and abandoned fields.

REMARKS: This species spends most of its time under protective cover. It will not bite if handled, but it may wiggle and discharge foul smelling liquid from its vent. Occasionally this snake may play dead if disturbed. The female gives birth to live young. The name *elegans* means elegant.

SNAKES

196

VENOMOUS SNAKES

Prairie Rattlesnake

Broad-banded Copperhead

Western Diamond-backed Rattlesnake tail

Broad-banded Copperhead

Head showing heat sensitive pit and vertical pupil

Osage Copperhead

Juvenile Osage Copperheads showing yellow tail tips

Southern Copperhead

SNAKES

198

SIZE: 22-36 inches.

APPEARANCE: This heavy-bodied, venomous snake has weakly keeled dorsal scales (see Fig. 12b.) Its dorsal color is copper or reddish-brown possibly with a pinkish tinge. There are dark, dorsal, hourglass-shaped, brown bands edged in white. The narrowest part of the band is at the mid-dorsal area. On the wide, lateral part of the dark hourglass markings, the central region is lighter than the outer edge. The head lacks markings. The head is visibly wider than the neck. On either side of the face there are heat sensing pits between (but below) the eye and nostril. The eyes have vertical pupils (see Fig. 14b.) The belly is pale with some lateral dark mottling. There is a single anal plate and a single row of scales under the tail (see Fig. 13b.) There is no rattle. A male has more bands on the tail than a female and a fully grown male is larger than a fully grown female. A neonate has a yellow tail tip. The ground color of the Southern Copperhead is light gray and the some of the crossbands may not meet at the midline. The ground color of the Osage Copperhead is a light copper, but is darker than the ground color of the Southern Copperhead and some of the crossbands may be offset at the midline. The Broad-banded Copperhead has crossbands that are nearly as wide at the mid-dorsal line as on the sides. These crossbands are darker reddish-brown in color than in the other subspecies and the crossbands always meet at the midline.

SIMILAR SPECIES: Non-venomous snakes lack vertical pupils and heat-sensing pits. Additionally, hog-nosed snakes have upturned snouts and watersnakes have longer tails, strongly keeled dorsal scales, and dark vertical lines on their upper lips. A young Copperhead has a narrow, dark line through the eye and a young Cottonmouth has a wide, dark band through each eye.

FOOD: Mice, birds, frogs, reptiles, and insects, especially cicadas.

HABITAT: Woodlands and mountainous areas near water.

REMARKS: Venomous to humans. The bite is rarely fatal, but causes local tissue damage. Nevertheless, medical attention should be sought for all Copperhead bites. This snake is nocturnal in warm weather and diurnal in cool weather. It is relatively nonaggressive and will not strike unless cornered. It has no rattles, but if disturbed it will vibrate its tail against dry leaves or grass and make a rattling sound. Because of its coloring, a Copperhead blends into its environment extremely well. A Copperhead hunts by ambushing its prey and may sit in the same spot for days waiting for prey. Rodents are injected with venom, quickly released, and then tracked by the snake using its keen sense of smell. Releasing the victim protects the snake from retaliation. Non-rodent prey are held in the snake's mouth until the venom overtakes them. Young use the yellow tail to lure in curious prey items. A Copperhead replaces its fangs periodically. Males sometimes combat each other over access to a breeding female. A female gives birth to live young. *Agkistrodon* means curved teeth, *laticinctus* means broad-banded, and *phaeogaster* means dark belly.

SUBSPECIES: Broad-banded Copperhead (*Agkistrodon contortrix laticinctus*), central Oklahoma; Southern Copperhead (*Agkistrodon contortrix contortrix*), extreme southeastern Oklahoma; Osage Copperhead (*Agkistrodon contortrix phaeogaster*), northeastern Oklahoma. The Broad-banded Copperhead has wide intergrade zones with the other subspecies in Oklahoma.

Adult

Juvenile

SIZE: 20-42 inches.

APPEARANCE: The dark back of this snake is not well patterned, except in juveniles. The dorsal scales are weakly keeled (see Fig. 12b.) The pupils are vertical slits (see Fig. 14b.) The head is visibly wider than the neck. There is a dark wide stripe from the neck through the eye and up to the tip of the snout, this is most easily seen in juveniles. There is a heat sensitive pit between (but below) the eye and nostril on either side of the face (see Fig. 14b.) There is a white line on the upper lip. The ground color of the belly is light, but the belly has many large dark blotches that make it look dark. There is a single row of scales under the tail, a single anal plate, (see Fig. 13b) and no rattle. The neonate has a yellow to yellow-green tail tip.

SIMILAR SPECIES: A watersnake has a double row of scales under the tail, no facial pits, and a divided anal plate. The Copperhead has a coppery color and lacks a wide, dark stripe through the eye.

FOOD: Amphibians, fish, snakes, lizards, turtles, small mammals, and birds. Juveniles eat mostly frogs.

HABITAT: Near a permanent source of water but will occasionally make long overland movements to new bodies of water.

REMARKS: Venomous to humans. Most retreat in the presence of a human. Never try to handle this species, the bite can be lethal! Fortunately, it rarely is. If bitten, medical attention should still be sought immediately. Contrary to myth, the Cottonmouth can and will bite underwater. Unlike most venomous snakes, it will hang on to its underwater prey to prevent losing it. When an adult eats a mammal, it injects the prey, releases it, and then tracks it. This protects the snake from being seriously injured by the mammal. The fangs are shed and replaced periodically. The bright tail tip of the juvenile is used to lure in prey. Despite the lack of rattles, if irritated this snake will vibrate its tail against dry grass or leaves and make a rattling sound. Normally it is nocturnal, but in cool weather it may be diurnal. The female gives birth to live young. The Cottonmouth often swims with its head, neck, and back out of the water, while non-venomous watersnakes normally swim with only the head and neck out of the water, but this should not be the sole means of identification. The Cottonmouth has a very large lung, which gives it buoyancy. This snake is sometimes called a water mocassin. Usually it will open the mouth at an intruder and expose the cottony white mouth, which is how the species got its common name, Cottonmouth. *Agkistrodon* means curved teeth, *piscivorus* means fish eater and *leucostoma* means white mouth.

Adult showing white "cotton" mouth

Photos showing color variations

Juvenile

Rattlesnake skull showing position of fangs

SIZE: 30-72 inches.

APPEARANCE: This rattlesnake has dark diamond-shaped, dorsal blotches edged with white. Posteriorly these blotches are indistinct. The ground color is gray or brown and the dorsal scales are keeled (see Fig. 12b.) A light line extends from the eye to the rear corner of the mouth. On each side of the face there is a heat sensitive pit between (but below) the eye and nostril. The pupil is vertical (see Fig. 14b.) The head has many small scales on its top mid-portion and is visibly wider than the neck. The tail has large rattles. The tail has broad white and black bands and the male has more black bands (five or more) than the female (three or less). Individuals with four black bands are about evenly split between male and female. The plain belly is white to cream. There is a single anal plate and a single row of scales under the tail (see Fig. 13b.)

SIMILAR SPECIES: A Prairie Rattlesnake has brownish blotches that become crossbands at the rear of the body and a white line that goes from the eye to above and past the rear corner of the mouth. A Timber Rattlesnake lacks a light line on the side of the head. In Oklahoma, only the Western Diamond-backed Rattlesnake has the bold black and white bands on the tail. A non-venomous snake lacks a rattle, vertical pupils, and heat sensitive pits.

FOOD: Rodents, rabbits, lizards, and ground-dwelling birds. Mammals are the main food.

HABITAT: Found in arid areas, rocky outcrops, and bluffs.

REMARKS: Venomous to humans. This is our largest rattlesnake and one of the largest snakes in Oklahoma. Its size allows it to inject a large quantity of venom, which may be fatal, especially in children. If bitten, medical attention should still be sought immediately. The young are born with venom. This species is often known as the "coon tail rattler." Because a male has a longer tail than a female, females normally have fewer dark bands on the tail than males. Like most snakes, it will avoid confrontation if possible, but it is rather aggressive and usually will rattle and may strike if disturbed. The fangs are shed and replaced periodically. This species is an ambush hunter and will wait for a prey item to come to it. This species hibernates in large numbers in dens. In the summer it is nocturnal and in cooler weather it is diurnal. Males will enter into combat with each other over access to reproductive females. The female gives birth to live young. This is a game species with a restricted open hunting season. *Crotalus* refers to rattling the tail.

SIZE: 35-54 inches.

APPEARANCE: This snake has dark bar-shaped or rectangular crossbands posteriorly and dark blotches near the head. The dorsal ground color is tan or yellow, but may be black. Some have a rusty-red colored mid-dorsal stripe and used to be called "canebreak rattlesnakes." Dorsal scales are keeled (see Fig. 12b.) The tail is dark, patternless, and has large rattles. The head is triangular and wider than the neck. Scales in the top mid-portion of the head are very small. A thick, dark line runs from the eye to the back corner of the mouth. There is a heat sensitive pit on either side of its face between (but below) the eye and nostril. The pupil is vertical (see Fig. 14b.) The belly is light gray or whitish and has some small dark spots near the edges. There is a single anal plate and a single row of scales under the tail (see Fig. 13b.) Males get bigger than females, and there is sexual dimorphism in color: males are usually yellow; females are usually black.

SIMILAR SPECIES: The Western Diamond-backed Rattlesnake has white-edged, diamond-shaped, dorsal blotches, and a black and white banded tail. A non-venomous snake lacks a rattle, vertical pupils, and heat sensitive pits.

FOOD: Small mammals (mostly squirrels, rabbits, rats, and mice), some birds, and snakes.

HABITAT: Rocky woodland hillsides and swampy wetlands.

REMARKS: Venomous, bites to humans are rare but can be fatal. If bitten, seek medical attention immediately. Young are born with venom. This ambush hunter will coil beside a fallen log and wait for rodents to run along the log. It injects prey with venom and trails it by smell. It relies on crypsis to defend itself. This species is called the "velvet tail." It may hibernate in large numbers in dens. During hot weather, it is nocturnal and diurnal in cool weather. A female gives birth to live young. Fangs are shed and replaced periodically. This is a game species with restricted open hunting season and may be declining in number. *Crotalus* refers to rattling the tail and *horridus* refers to the venomous bite.

SIZE: 34-45 inches.

APPEARANCE: The ground color of the Prairie Rattlesnake is brown, gray, or yellow, often with a greenish cast. Anteriorly, the midline of the back has brown blotches with dark edges; on the tail these change to dark brown bands. Its dorsal scales are keeled (see Fig. 12b.) A light line extends from each eye past and above the rear corner of its mouth. The head has many small scales on the top mid-portion and is visibly wider than the neck. The pupil is vertical. On either side of the face there is a heat-sensing pit between (but below) the eye and nostril (see Fig. 14b.) The tail has large rattles. An adult male has a longer, thicker tail than a female and has more bands on the tail than a female. The plain belly is white to cream. There is a single row of scales under the tail and a single anal plate (see Fig. 13b.)

SIMILAR SPECIES: The Western Diamond-backed Rattlesnake has distinct white and black banding on the tail and the white line goes from behind the eye to the rear corner of the jaw. A non-venomous snake lacks a rattle, vertical pupils, and heat sensing pits.

FOOD: Rodents, other small mammals, lizards, and ground-dwelling birds. Adults mainly eat mammals and juveniles mainly eat lizards.

HABITAT: Rocky outcrops or canyons, open grasslands, and prairie dog towns.

REMARKS: Venomous to humans. This snake has the most toxic venom of all Oklahoma snakes and is more aggressive than the Timber Rattlesnake. If bitten, seek medical attention immediately. It injects prey with venom and trails it by smell. The fangs are shed periodically and replaced. It may hibernate in communal dens. In the summer it is nocturnal and often spends its days in rodent burrows. During cooler weather it is active during the day and evening. Males do combat with each other to win reproductive females. The female gives birth to live young. This is an Oklahoma game species and has a restricted open hunting season. *Crotalus* means it rattles its tail.

SNAKES

Photo showing
color variation

SIZE: 18-26 inches.

APPEARANCE: The ground color is tan or gray. There are mid-dorsal, dark brown blotches edged in white and two or three rows of small, often faded, blotches on each side. The head is visibly wider than the neck. The dorsal scales are keeled (see Fig. 12b) and the head has nine large scales forming an oval on top of the head between the eyes and nostrils. On either side of the face is a heat sensitive pit between (but below) the eye and nostril. The pupil is vertical (see Fig. 14b.) The tail has small rattles. A male has more bands on the tail than a female. A fully grown male is larger than a fully grown female. The neonate may have a yellow tailtip. The belly is light gray with some dark mottling along the edges. There is a single anal plate and a single row of scales under the tail (see Fig. 13b.)

SIMILAR SPECIES: Other rattlesnakes have a mixture of large and small scales on the head. The Pygmy Rattlesnake has a mid-dorsal rust colored stripe. A non-venomous snake lacks a rattle, vertical pupils, and heat sensing pits.

FOOD: Adults eat lizards, rodents, frogs, and small snakes. Juveniles mostly eat small snakes.

HABITAT: Hillsides, prairies, and grasslands. Usually near a water source.

REMARKS: Venomous to humans, if bitten seek medical attention immediately, although a bite does not normally result in death. This snake injects prey with venom. When disturbed it may rattle its tail, but the small rattles make little sound. It is fast and quick to strike. A juvenile may wave its tail to attract prey. Fangs are shed and replaced periodically. It is nocturnal in summer and diurnal in cooler weather. A female gives birth to live young. It is known as the "sand rattler" or "ground rattler." It is a game species with a restricted open hunting season. Throughout its U.S. range, this species is declining due to habitat loss and poor land management. *Sistrurus* means this snake has a rattle on its tail, *catenatus* means having a chain-like pattern, and *tergeminus* refers to the three rows of blotches.

SIZE: 15-20 inches.

APPEARANCE: The ground color of the Western Pygmy Rattlesnake is gray. It has short, wide, mid-dorsal, dark blotches, many of which appear to be rectangular bars, and one or two rows of small, dark, faded blotches on each side. A male may have a lighter ground color than a female. In most individuals a thin reddish to chestnut mid-dorsal stripe extends through the dorsal blotches. The dorsal scales are keeled (see Fig. 12b.) There are nine large scales forming an oval on top of the head between the eyes and nostrils. It has a heat sensitive pit between (but below) the eye and nostril on each side of the face (see Fig. 14b.) There is a dark bar on each side of the head from the eye to the back corner of the mouth. The pupil is vertical. The head is visibly wider than the neck. The tail is thin and the rattles are small. A neonate may have yellow on the end of the tail. The belly is cream colored with many dark blotches or bars. There is a single anal plate and a single row of scales under the tail (see Fig. 13b.)

SIMILAR SPECIES: A Massasauga has no mid-dorsal stripe, has larger rattles, and a thicker tail. A Massasauga's blotches are larger and closer together than the Western Pygmy Rattlesnake's. Other rattlesnakes have a mixture of large and small scales on head.

FOOD: Lizards, snakes, frogs, mice, and invertebrates.

HABITAT: Variable and often found in association with pine trees.

REMARKS: Venomous to humans. It injects prey with venom and eats it once it dies. This small snake has a rattle that sounds like an insect buzz, and can be heard only if you are near it. It is locally known as the "ground rattler." This rattlesnake rarely bites humans and is not as toxic as other rattlesnakes, although seek medical attention if a bite occurs. The fangs are shed and replaced periodically. The female gives birth to live young. *Sistrurus* is a reference to the tail with rattles.

SNAKES

Glossary

Aggregation - a group of individuals

Anal plate - the scale in front of the vent (see Fig. 13)

Anterior - situated toward the front

Anuran - frog or toad

Aquatic - primarily inhabiting water

Arboreal - living on or among trees

Autotomize (autotomy) - break off from the body

Barbels - slender protuberances around the chin and/or throat

Bask - to sit in the sun to warm up

Boss - rounded, swollen area on the forehead

Carapace - upper part of turtle shell, which contains the ribs

Carnivorous - meat (and insect) eating

Carrion - dead and decaying flesh

Cirrus (Cirri, plural) - a projection of skin hanging down from the tip of the nasolabial groove in some of the salamanders of the genus *Eurycea* (see Fig. 2)

Costal Groove - vertical grooves on the sides of most salamanders located between the front and back legs (see Fig. 1)

Courtship - behavioral acts that precede copulation

Cranial crests - raised ridges on the head (see Fig. 4)

Crypsis (cryptic) - blending in well with the background

Desiccation - dehydrate or dry out

Dewlap - throat fan

Direct development - in salamanders where the juvenile hatches out of the egg as a miniature replica of the adult; there is no free-living larval stage

Diurnal - active in the day

Dorsal (dorsum) - back of an animal

Dorsolateral - between the midline of the back and the side of the animal

Dorsolateral fold - a line of raised glandular skin between the midline of the back and the side of the animal (see Fig. 3)

Ecomorph - a local variety whose appearance is determind by environmental factors such as soil color.

Eft - terrestrial life stage of a newt

Estivate - to pass the summer in a state of inactivity

Femoral pores - glandular openings on the underside of a lizard's thigh

Gravid - pregnant or with eggs

Herbivorous - plant eating

Herpetologist - a scientist who studies amphibians and reptiles

Intergrade - the offspring produced when two different subspecies of the same species mate; the offspring show characteristics of the two parental subspecies

Invertebrates - animals lacking a backbone such as worms and insects; all amphibians and reptiles are vertebrates

Isopod - small crustacean such as a pillbug, roly-poly, or sowbug

Keeled scales - rough, dorsal scales of a snake or lizard; a raised ridge runs longitudinally down the scale (see Fig. 12)

Keeled tail - a thin tail with a high dorsal ridge; found in aquatic salamanders and used in swimming

Keels - ridges

Labial - pertaining to the lips (see Figs. 9, 10, and 15)

Larva (plural Larvae) - aquatic, gilled young of amphibians

Lateral - on the side

Longitudinal - going the length of the body

Marginal scutes - scales on the edge of a turtle carapace (see Fig. 6)

Metamorphosis - change from larva to adult or from larva to eft in the case of the Central Newt

Mid-dorsal - running down the middle of the back

Mottled - marked by colored blotches

Nasolabial groove - groove extending from the nostril to the lip, which is used to pick up odors (see Fig. 2)

Neonate - newborns or hatchlings

Nocturnal - active at night.

Omnivorous - plant and animal eating

Parotoid glands - a pair of large glands behind the eyes of a toad (see Fig. 4)

Permeable - the ability of a substance to cross a barrier such as the skin

Plastron (plastral) - lower part of turtle shell equivalent to "breast bone" (see Figs. 6b and 8)

Posterior - situated toward the rear

Prehensile - can grasp or wrap around

Rear fanged - the posterior tooth in each upper tooth row is enlarged and may deliver a venom

Reticulate - network of lines

Scutes - scales on a turtle shell or ventral scales of a snake

Serrated - saw-toothed

Sexual dimorphism - visible external differences between the two sexes such as size or color; for example male Collared Lizards are green and females are tan

Spade - structure on underside of hind foot of some toads and frogs that is used for digging (see Fig. 5)

Spermathea - a site for sperm storage in female salamanders

Spermatophore - a sperm packet released by male salamanders

Subspecies - two or more closely related forms of the same species (usually with some geographic separation)

Tadpole - aquatic larva of frogs and toads

Temperature dependent sex determination - the sex of a hatchling is determined by the temperature at which it is incubated; found in alligators, many turtles, and some lizards

Terrestrial - primarily inhabiting land

Territory - a defended area in which an animal lives

Tympanum - eardrum (see Figs. 3d and 4)

Type locality - the locality from which the specimen used to describe the species was taken

Unisexual - of one sex (all members of a population are female)

Vent - a common opening through which the products of the reproductive, excretory, and digestive tracts are expelled; often called cloaca

Ventral (venter) - belly of an animal

Vocal sac - inflatable pouch on the throat of male frogs and toads

Warts - round glands on the skin

References

GENERAL HERPETOLOGY TEXTBOOKS

Pough, F.H., R.M. Andrews, J.E. Cadle, M.L. Crump, A.H. Savitzky, and K.D. Wells. 2004. Herpetology. Third ed. Prentice Hall, Upper Saddle River, New Jersey.

L.J. Vitt, and J.P. Caldwell. 2009. Herpetology. An Introductory Biology of Amphibians and Reptiles. Third ed. Academic Press, San Diego, California.

FURTHER REFERENCES

Collins, J.T., S.L. Collins, and T.W. Taggart. 2010. Amphibians, Reptiles, and Turtles in Kansas. Eagle Mountain Publishing, Eagle Mountain, UT.

Committee on Standard English and Scientific Names. 2008. Scientific and standard English names of amphibians and reptiles of North America north of Mexico, with comments regarding confidence in our understanding. Society for the Study of Amphibians and Reptiles Herpetological Circular #37: 1-84.

Conant, R. and J.T. Collins. 1998. A Field Guide to Reptiles and Amphibians of Eastern and Central North America. Third ed, expanded. Houghton Mifflin Co., Boston.

Dodd, C.K. 2001. North American Box Turtles: A Natural History. University of Oklahoma Press. Norman, Oklahoma.

Ernst, C.H. and J.E. Lovich. 2009. Turtles of the United States and Canada (2nd ed.). Johns Hopkins University Press. Baltimore, Maryland. 827 p.

Fitch, H.S. 1999. A Kansas Snake Community: Composition and Changes over 50 Years. Krieger Publishing Co. Malabar, Florida.

Garrett, J.M. and D.G. Barker. 1987. A Field Guide to Reptiles and Amphibians of Texas. Texas Monthly Press. Austin, Texas,

Gibbons, J.W. and M.E. Dorcas. 2004. North American Watersnakes: A Natural History. University of Oklahoma Press. Norman, Oklahoma.

Hammerson, G.A. 1999. Amphibians and Reptiles in Colorado, Second ed. Univ. Press of Colorado. Niwot, Colorado.

Johnson, T.R. 2000. The Amphibians and Reptiles of Missouri. Revised and Expanded Second ed. Missouri Dept. of Conservation. Jefferson City, Missouri.

Petranka, J.W. 1998. Salamanders of the United States and Canada. Smithsonian Institution Press. Washington, D.C.

Powell, R., J.T. Collins, and E.D. Hooper, Jr. 1998. A Key to Amphibians and Reptiles of the Continental United States and Canada. University of Kansas Press. Lawrence, Kansas.

Rossman, D.A., N.B. Ford, and R.A. Seigel. 1996. The Garter Snakes: Evolution and Ecology. Univ. of Oklahoma Press. Norman, Oklahoma.

Stebbins, R.C. 2003. A Field Guide to Western Reptiles and Amphibians. Third ed. Houghton and Mifflin Co. Boston.

Trauth, S.E., H.W. Robison, and M.V. Plummer. 2004. The Amphibians and Reptiles of Arkansas. University of Arkansas Press. Fayetteville, Arkansas

Webb, R.G. 1970. Reptiles of Oklahoma. University of Oklahoma Press. Norman, Oklahoma.

Werler, J.E. and J.R. Dixon. 2000. Texas Snakes: Identification, distribution, and natural history. University of Texas Press. Austin, Texas.

Wright, J.W. and L.J. Vitt. 1993. Biology of Whiptail Lizards (Genus Cnemidophorus). Oklahoma Mus. Nat. Hist., Norman, Oklahoma.